VICTORIAN BRITAIN
A MASTER FILE
KEY STAGES 2 AND 3

General editors
D. C. Perkins, BA (Hons), MEd, PhD (Wales) and E J Perkins, BSc (Hons), MEd
Illustrations by Anthony James

MASTER FILES are planned for use in the classroom. Each consists of teachers' notes, pupils' resource material, worksheets, ideas for project work and assessment tables. Each book covers part of the National Curriculum in depth allowing the teacher to decide the amount of material to use according to the age and ability of the children.

DOMINO BOOKS (WALES) LTD
SWANSEA SA1 1FN
Tel. 0792 459378 Fax. 0792 466337

ISBN 1 85772 077 6

CONTENTS 1

TEACHERS' NOTES AND RESOURCES

Compiled by experienced teachers, **Victorian Britain, Master File,** is a comprehensive coverage of the material needed for the National Curriculum. At Key Stage 2, the book covers the 'Life in Modern Britain and Wales' unit dealing with the living and working conditions of British people in the 19th. century including the UK as a growing industrial nation, sanitation and disease, middle class family life, child labour, schools, and the roles of churches and chapels. The book is also useful for historical themes such as houses and households, and land transport. At Key Stage 3, the book covers industrialisation and its effects, population changes, the growth of towns and developments in transport. The effects of developments and changes on living and working conditions and Victorian reforms in public health, education and the Poor Law are also considered.

Pupils' Resources/Worksheets Contents on next page

CONTENTS 2
PUPILS' RESOURCES/WORKSHEETS

THE VICTORIANS

THE VICTORIANS CROSS-CURRICULAR LINKS AND ACTIVITIES

ENGLISH
- Cloze tests
- Sequencing
- Letters
- Imaginative writing
- Reporting
- Speech-making
- Word searches
- Word puzzles
- Victorian writers/novelists
- Story telling

MATHEMATICS
- Time charts
- Population changes
- Old money £.s.d.
- Extent of the Empire
- Price movements
- Roads/transport
- Emigration
- Wages

SCIENCE
- Medical advances
- Scientific discoveries
- Growth of industrialisation
- Building techniques
- Engineering techniques
- Development of towns
- Town planning
- Development of basic sanitation
- Public reform
- Road technology
- Transport developments

ART
- Victorian design
- Victorian artefacts
- Fashion
- Victorian jewellery
- Decorations
- Victorian Art
- Pre-Raphaelites

LAW
- Victorian law
- Crimes
- Punishments
- Major legal changes
- Status of women and children
- The police
- The workhouse régime

GEOGRAPHY
- Map work
- Explorers
- Spread of British Empire
- Overseas colonies
- Discoveries in foreign lands
- Exploitation of overseas dependencies
- Foreign travel

RELIGION
- Church-going
- Chapels
- Role in family life
- Birth
- Death
- Burial
- Missionaries

SOCIOLOGY
- Class structure
- Social structure
- Children in Victorian times
- Economics
- Education
- Status of men and women
- Voting rights
- Co-operative movement
- Labour Party
- Employment

TEACHERS' NOTES AND RESOURCES

HOW TO USE YOUR MASTER FILE

For many experienced teachers these few lines will seem superfluous. This book is planned to introduce pupils to the history of Britain. The degree of difficulty varies throughout the book. Following the National Curriculum guidelines, it is especially helpful for those between 7 - 11 and 11 - 13 years and it provides a background for older children as they proceed to more advanced work.

1. All the material in this book is photocopiable as defined on page 1. This means that all the material can be used in any way you wish in the classroom situation. Drawings may be photocopied and adapted for further work.

2. Covering sections of the master copies with plain paper enables resource material to be used in different ways. The questions may, if you wish, be omitted and you can use the drawings with your own questions.

3. Reduction of the A4 master copies to A5 means that they can be pasted in children's exercise books. The master copies can also be enlarged to A3 to make it easier for students to work on them as a group.

4. Some of your photocopies can be cut up to make additional puzzles and games.

5. It is intended that material be used at different levels depending on the ages and abilities of your pupils.

6. It may be possible to use some of the Teachers' Notes directly with more advanced and brighter students.

7. Some of the worksheets and resources are more difficult than others and the teacher has to decide the selection of appropriate material.

8. Some of the copy in the teachers' resources may be used in other ways, e.g. as cloze tests, sequencing exercises and so on.

9. Much of the completed work may be used as visual aids around the classroom.

10. Project work may be done individually, in groups and/or with teacher participation.

We hope you enjoy using this book and welcome any comments.

CHRONOLOGY OF EVENTS

Introduce pupils to the Victorian Age by explaining that history pinpoints time by using the words *age* or *period* and the name of a person or event. Queen Victoria reigned from 1837 - 1901. The time immediately before, that is, the Georgian Period (1714 - 1830) was named after the four Kings who ruled Britain then - George I, II, III and IV. Other examples are the Tudor and Stuart Periods.

Set the scene for the study by saying that during Victorian times, Britain became the most powerful country in the world - it had the largest Empire (spread over one-fifth of the world's surface) and ruled a quarter of all peoples. So much happened during the period that it can only be dealt with by using a topic approach. The main themes of study are dealt with in some detail in this book.

Time-lines are included where helpful and the children could be encouraged to produce their own in periods of 10 years, i.e. time-line decades. They may produce such material on a computer. They may also be compiled under headings such as Education, Medicine, Factory Legislation, Public Health Acts, Science and so on. The children may add their own drawings and photographs to these. Such collections make attractive and informative displays. The time-line below covers many of the major events.

A VICTORIAN TIME-LINE OF EVENTS

1819 Birth of Victoria.

1832 First Parliamentary Reform Act.
(The first step towards democracy.)

1834 Slavery abolished in all British Colonies.
Poor Law Amendment Act introduced a new system of poor relief.

1835 Town councils permitted to set up their own police forces to keep order.

1837 William IV died. Victoria crowned Queen.

1840 Penny post introduced.
First co-operative shop started in Rochdale.
Queen Victoria married Prince Albert.

1842 Mines Act ended child and female labour in coalmines.

1844 The working day restricted to 12 hours for women and young people.

1845 Potato famine in Ireland.

1847 First anaesthetic introduced by James Simpson.
10 Hour Act introduced a maximum working day of 10 hours for women and young people in the cotton industry.

1848 First Public Health Act introduced by Edwin Chadwick.

1851 The Great Exhibition suggested by Prince Albert opened in Hyde Park.
Singer introduced the first practical sewing machine.

1852 Morse Code used in telegraphy.
David Livingstone left England to explore Africa (the Zambesi).

1853 Anaesthetics came to be used widely after Queen Victorian was helped in childbirth.
Vaccination against smallpox became compulsory.

1854 Britain took part in the Crimean War.

1855 Florence Nightingale cared for troops at Scutari. Hygiene brought to nursing.

CHRONOLOGY OF EVENTS

[illegible]

A VICTORIAN TIME-LINE OF EVENTS

[illegible]

1856 End of Crimean War.

1857 Indian Mutiny.

1859 Charles Darwin wrote 'Origin of Species' about evolution.
De Lesseps began work on the Suez Canal.

1861 Death of Prince Albert.
American Civil War began.

1862 Revised Code of Education - payment by results.
Abraham Lincoln abolished slavery in the USA.

1863 Rules for Association Football laid down.

1865 Joseph Lister discovered the first antiseptic.
Red Flag Act put a speed limit on 'horseless carriages'.
The American Civil War ended.
President Lincoln assassinated.

1866 Dr Barnardo began his work for orphans.

1867 Working men in the boroughs allowed to vote in parliamentary elections.

1868 Foundation of the Trades Union Congress. Gangs Act prohibited the employment of children under 8 on farms.

1869 Suez Canal opened.

1870 Forsters' Education Act introduced State Elementary Schools for children aged 5 - 10.
Half-penny post began.

1871 Legal recognition accorded to Trade Unions.
Stanley located Livingstone in Africa.
First F. A. Cup competition.

1872 Typewriter invented.

1874 Factory Acts introduced a 10 hour working day.
Minimum age for child workers.
English lawn tennis started.

1875 Public Health Acts introduced by Disraeli as well as other social reforms.

1876 Disraeli bought shares in the Suez Canal Company.
Queen Victoria became Empress of India.
School attendance made compulsory.
New inventions included Bell's telephone, Edison's phonograph and Bissell's carpet sweeper.

1878 Electric lighting in London.

1879 Zulu War started.
Swan and Edison invented the carbon filament for electric lights.

1880 First Boer War.

1882 Married women allowed to own property.
The first Test Match between England and Australia.

1884 Parliamentary vote granted to agricultural labourers.

1885 General Gordon killed at Khartoum.
Daimler invented high-speed internal combustion engine in Germany. The first motor bike invented.

1886 Gas mantle invented.

1887 Queen Victoria's Golden Jubilee.
Coal Mines Regulation Act meant boys under 13 could not work in the mines.

1888 Pneumatic tyre developed.
Kodak box-camera invented.

1889 Dockers' strike.
An act passed to protect children from cruelty.

1890 Motion pictures began in the USA.
First 'tube' railway opened in London.

1891 Wireless telegraphy began.

1893 Aspirin introduced.

1895 X-rays discovered by Röntgen.
First motor car exhibition in London.
Gillette invented the safety razor.

1896 First Olympic Games held in Greece (Athens).
Red Flag Act for motor cars repealed. Maximum speed raised to 14 mph.

1897 Queen Victoria's Diamond Jubilee.

1898 Radium discovered by Pierre and Marie Curie.
Sudan conquered.

1900 Cadbury established the Bournville Village Trust.

1901 Death of Queen Victoria.

As well as this time-line of events, it is useful to establish the position of Queen Victoria in the line of succession.

QUEEN VICTORIA'S GENEALOGICAL TABLE

This tree shows the main branches of the royal family leading up to, during, and following on from Queen Victoria.

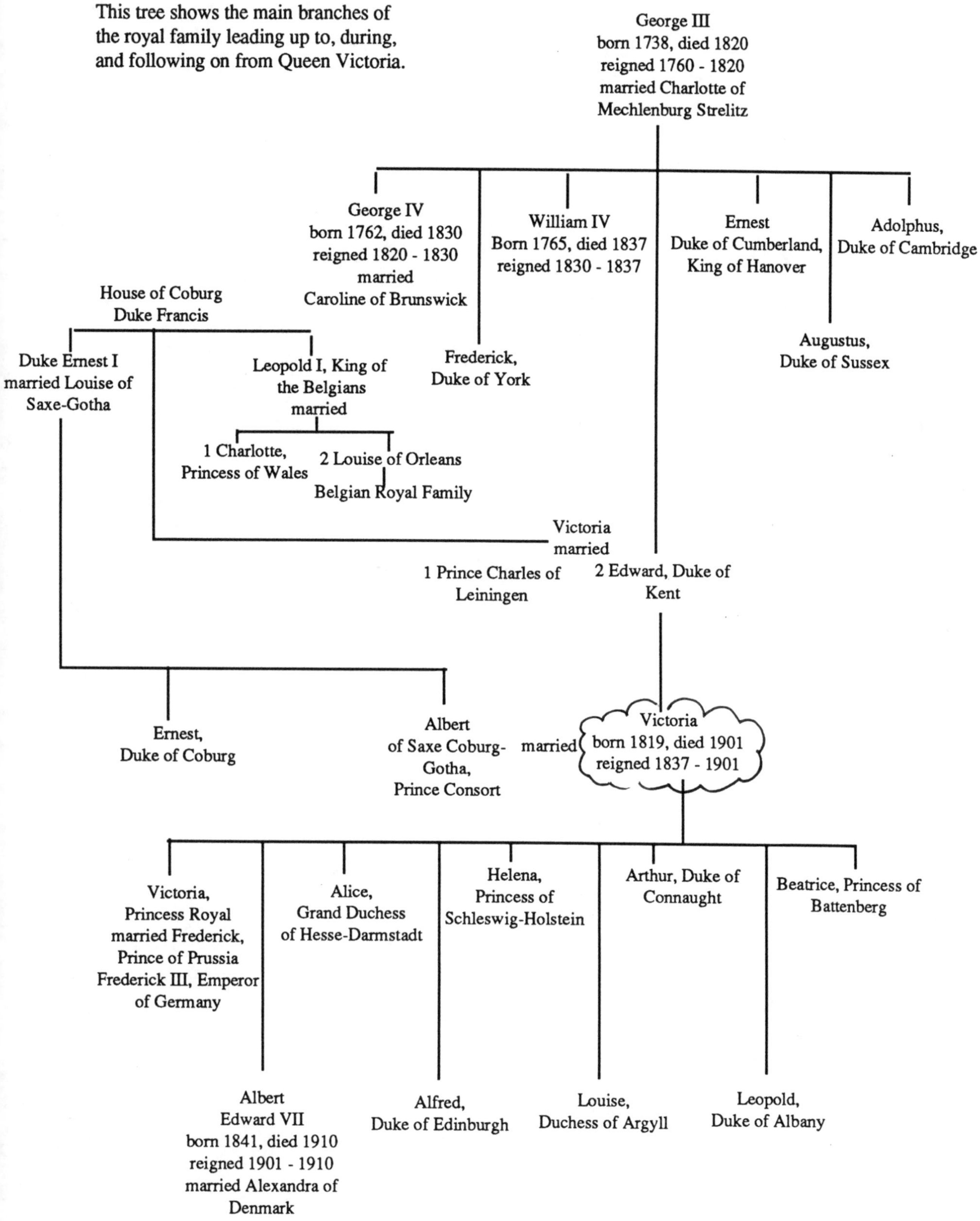

QUEEN VICTORIA'S GENEALOGICAL TABLE

A shortened version (to paste in the children's exercise books) is

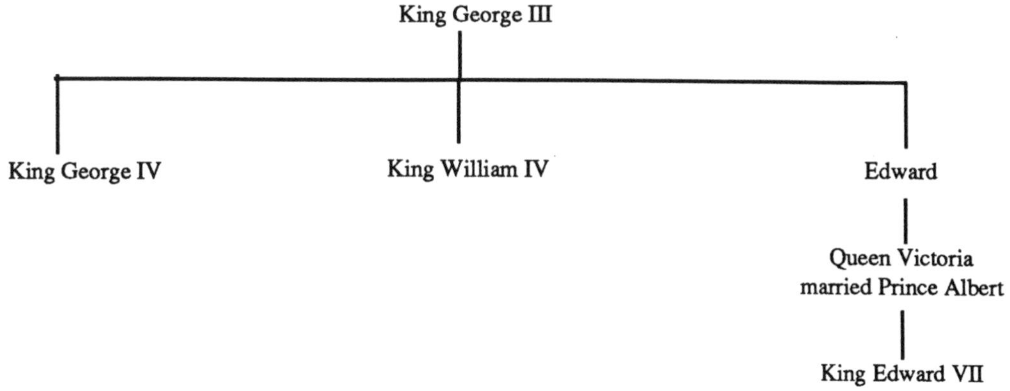

LEARNING ABOUT THE PAST

Children need to know how historians find out about earlier times: Queen Victoria and her subjects, their triumphs and tribulations. We build up a knowledge of the past from a variety of sources and the picture is continually changing as additional evidence unfolds, more research is undertaken and new techniques enable us to make more accurate deductions. Resources include the following.

1. Books, newspapers and written records. These include contemporary reading matter. Victorian copies of, for example, *The Times* newspaper, *The Illustrated London News* and the magazine, *Punch.*

2. Contemporary letters and diaries, e.g. *Letters of Queen Victoria 1837 - 1861.*

3. Government records and documents, e.g. *Hansard,* Proposed Bills and Actual Acts of Parliament.

4. Paintings, drawings, lithographs and carvings from Victorian times.

5. Photographs and films: remember the first photographs appeared in Victorian times.

6. 'Within living memory' - information available from personal accounts and records. Some people are still living who lived at the end of Victoria's reign. Tales recounted by great grandparents are invaluable as are family diaries, letters and photographs.

7. Sound recordings. This source is limited because sound recordings were not possible until late in the Victorian age.

8. The work of Victorian novelists, e.g. Charles Dickens.

9. Directories and parish records from the past, school attendance registers, account books used by Victorian businesses.

10. Anything built in Victorian times or made then. Objects used by the Victorians including household utensils and clothes, watches and jewellery.

Explain to the children how these sources differ from those usually used by historians (archaeology, aerial photography, radio-active carbon dating etc.) and make a distinction between more 'recent' history and more 'distant' history. Suggest the children look for historical material in their own homes or in the homes of their grandparents. It is amazing what they will find. Encourage them to bring relevant material to school (but they must have permission from home - some items may be valuable or have particular value for their owners). Organise an 'Antiques Roadshow' on BBC lines. Let the children guess what some of the strange objects were used for. Distinguish carefully between primary (original) sources and secondary sources.

VICTORIAN BRITAIN - LEARNING THROUGH TOPICS

Explain how the Victorian Age comprises a great deal of political, economic and social history and that many developments occurred. A study of the period in detail could take many years and thus the best way to tackle it is through discussion and providing exercises on the main themes or topics.

WHO WAS VICTORIA? THE QUEEN, HER CONSORT AND BERTIE, LATER EDWARD VII

The future Queen Victoria was born on 24th. May, 1819. Her parents planned to christen their daughter Georgina Charlotte Augusta but this plan was frustrated by the Prince Regent's bad behaviour at the christening and she was named Alexandrina Victoria instead. As a child, Victoria was called 'Drina' at home. Her father, the Duke of Kent, died when she was only eight months old and she was looked after by her mother and a stern German governess, Baroness Lehzen. Fortunately for us, Victoria began to keep a diary in her early teens and we can learn a great deal about her from this.

As a young girl, Victoria was rarely left alone and seldom played with children of her own age. Her mother, the Duchess of Kent, was very protective and slept in her bedroom until Victoria was 18. Her mother believed she should be properly prepared for her future rôle as Queen of England and between 1832 and 1835 Victoria was sent on a series of journeys to North Wales, the Midlands, Yorkshire, East Anglia and the south coast. She described what she saw in her diary.

> *The Country is very desolate everywhere: there are coals about and the grass is quite blasted and black ... Everywhere [there are] smoking and burning coal heaps, intermingled with wretched huts and carts and ragged children.*

On the death of her uncle, William IV, Victoria became Queen. She was 18 and wrote in her diary (20th. June, 1837):

> *I was awoke at 6 o'clock by Mamma who told me that the Archbishop of Canterbury and Lord Coyngham were here and wished to see me. Lord Coyngham then acquainted me that my poor Uncle, the King, was no more, and had expired at 12 minutes past 2 this morning and consequently that I am Queen.*

Once Queen, Victoria had more freedom and began to enjoy herself. She took up horse-riding, went to the opera and theatre regularly and attended fêtes, banquets and concerts and stayed out late at fashionable balls.

Victoria's closest friend and advisor on political matters during these early formative years was the Prime Minister Lord Melbourne. In 1839 Victoria met her German cousin Prince Albert and her family felt that he would make an ideal husband. Fortunately,Victoria was attracted to him and they were married on 10 February, 1840. From this time until his death, Albert had an enormous influence on his wife. He insisted they spend time with their children and wanted as normal a family life as possible. Between 1841 and 1857 the royal couple had nine children, four sons and five daughters. They were extremely happy.

Victoria and Albert spent much of their time in Scotland at the royal estate they built at Balmoral. They were also fond of the Isle of Wight where they built and extended a new home called Osborne. In 1861, Albert died of typhoid fever. This was a tragedy for Victoria who mourned him for for the rest of her life. The Queen said, *The world is gone for me.* She insisted on wearing black clothes, refused to attend state occasions for many years and lived as a recluse at Balmoral or Osborne. In 1883 Victoria attended the wedding of her son Bertie and Princess Alexandra of Denmark but she became upset because the ceremony reminded her of her own marriage to Albert, and she did not stay long. Victoria celebrated her golden jubilee in 1887 her diamond jubilee in 1897. The Queen died at the age of 80 on 22 January, 1901.

Ensure the children know the main biographical details about Queen Victoria. They might prepare short notes of her life with the main details underlined. Pictures including the children's own drawings as well as photographs, illustrations from books and magazines like *The Illustrated London News* add interest to the work. You may be able to help their researches by obtaining early newspapers, magazines (*The Times* was first published in 1788) or jubilee material. The children should look for pictures of the Queen at different times in her life (as a young girl, aged 18, at the time of her marriage, at her wedding, at her golden and diamond jubilees). Use Victoria as a starting point to the study of Britain at this time. The children could then compile a comparative chart like the one on the next page.

At the beginning of Victoria's Reign (1837)	At the end of Victoria's Reign (1901)
The British Empire	
Parliamentary Reform	
Achievements in Public Health	
Developments in Science	
New Buildings	
Developments in Transport	
Developments in Medicine	
Industrial Developments	
Developments in Communications	
Developments in Employment (especially of women and children)	
Developments in Education	

The list is a long one. It adds interest to the study if you can get a copy of Victoria's diary - there is a copy of this at most public or university libraries. You can read excerpts from this to the children, especially those written at important stages in Victoria's life.

PRINCE ALBERT, CONSORT TO VICTORIA

At first, many people disliked Albert. He was a foreigner and people did not think he had this country's welfare at heart. But he proved to be a good husband to the Queen and a good ambassador for this country. For 21 years, Victoria was completely devoted to him. Although very strict and stern, he doted on their children. In 1853 for example, he brought a complete chalet from Switzerland as a playhouse for them. People soon came to respect him for his interest in the arts, education and science. He helped to reform the British army, encouraged museum building (especially the Natural History Museum and the Royal Albert Museum in London) and planned the Great Exhibition which opened in the Crystal Palace, Hyde Park on 1 May, 1851. It was a tragedy for the nation and Queen Victoria when he died prematurely in 1861 of typhoid fever.

QUEEN VICTORIA'S CHILDREN

Queen Victoria had a great influence on the destiny of Europe because so many of her children married into European royal families. She had nine children, forty grandchildren and twenty-nine great grandchildren. The extent of her influence can be estimated from the following table.

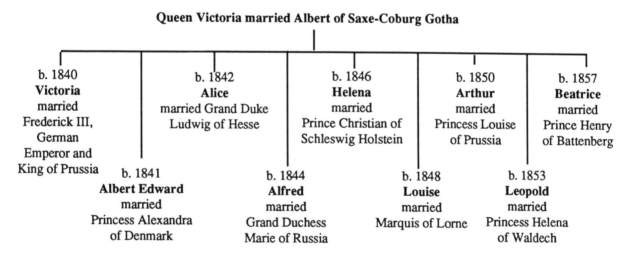

Queen Victoria married Albert of Saxe-Coburg Gotha

b. 1840 **Victoria** married Frederick III, German Emperor and King of Prussia

b. 1841 **Albert Edward** married Princess Alexandra of Denmark

b. 1842 **Alice** married Grand Duke Ludwig of Hesse

b. 1844 **Alfred** married Grand Duchess Marie of Russia

b. 1846 **Helena** married Prince Christian of Schleswig Holstein

b. 1848 **Louise** married Marquis of Lorne

b. 1850 **Arthur** married Princess Louise of Prussia

b. 1853 **Leopold** married Princess Helena of Waldech

b. 1857 **Beatrice** married Prince Henry of Battenberg

BERTIE, LATER EDWARD VII

Victoria's eldest son was born on 9 November, 1841, the first heir born to a reigning monarch since 1762. He was educated privately and then at the universities of Edinburgh, Oxford and Cambridge. Denied a position of state, he dissipated his energies in leisurely pursuits. He enjoyed hunting, went on safari up the Nile and in 1860 went on a tour of Canada. He was involved in several scandals with women - the Tranby Croft scandal and the Mordaunt divorce case were typical. In 1863 he married Alexandra of Denmark with whom he had three sons and three daughters. He died on 6 May, 1910 aged 68.

LIFE IN VICTORIAN TIMES

It is necessary to describe and discuss life in Victorian Britain. Explain that this means people's lives last century (the 19th. century).

The following illustrates the main points.

1. **Life in the early 1830s** was mainly based on the countryside. Agricultural work was the most important. Only about a third of the population lived in towns. But by mid-century (1850) this was changing as people in rural communities moved to the towns.

2. **'Free trade' had begun.** Since Tudor and Stuart times, British agriculture and manufacturing industries were protected from competition. As the 19th. century developed, this protection diminished.

3. **Generally, there was peace in Europe.** Even by 1850 there had been no major war in Europe for 35 years. By 1853 this had changed and Russian invaded Turkish territory - the Crimean War began.

4. **Many people were religious** and attendances at church (and chapel) were relatively high for the whole of the Victorian period.

5. **More people moved to the towns** to seek work in new trades, factories and industries. Women and young children worked long hours for very poor wages in unhealthy and dangerous mills and factories. The problems of the poor became worse in the towns.

6. **Family life** was important to the Victorians. They had large familes - the average size was 5 or 6 children.

7. **Class structure of society.** There was a clear demarcation between
   (a) the working classes,
   (b) the middle classes,
   (c) the upper classes.

8. **Education.** There was little education or schooling for young children at the start of this period. This changed as the century developed.

9. **There were major developments in this period in**
   (a) industrial inventions
   (b) scientific inventions
   (c) medicine
   (d) public health
   (e) transport
   (f) communications
   (g) agricultural techniques
   (h) education
   (i) political representation
   (j) industrial organisations

10. **The British Empire** grew from 1830 onwards. Compare the two maps on the next page.

These developments can be represented on a chart with all the class contributing. Illustrations and drawings all add interest, for example, it might begin like this:

CHART OF CHANGES AND DEVELOPMENTS IN VICTORIAN BRITAIN

1830s	**Developments**	**1901**
People lived mainly in the country. About a third lived in towns.	As industry developed people moved to the towns.	People lived mainly in towns.

Dominion - Land - belonging to sovereign/govt.

Colony - settlers in a new country/countries under rule by one mother country - ie Britain

THE BRITISH EMPIRE

THE GROWTH OF THE BRITISH EMPIRE IN THE NINETEENTH CENTURY

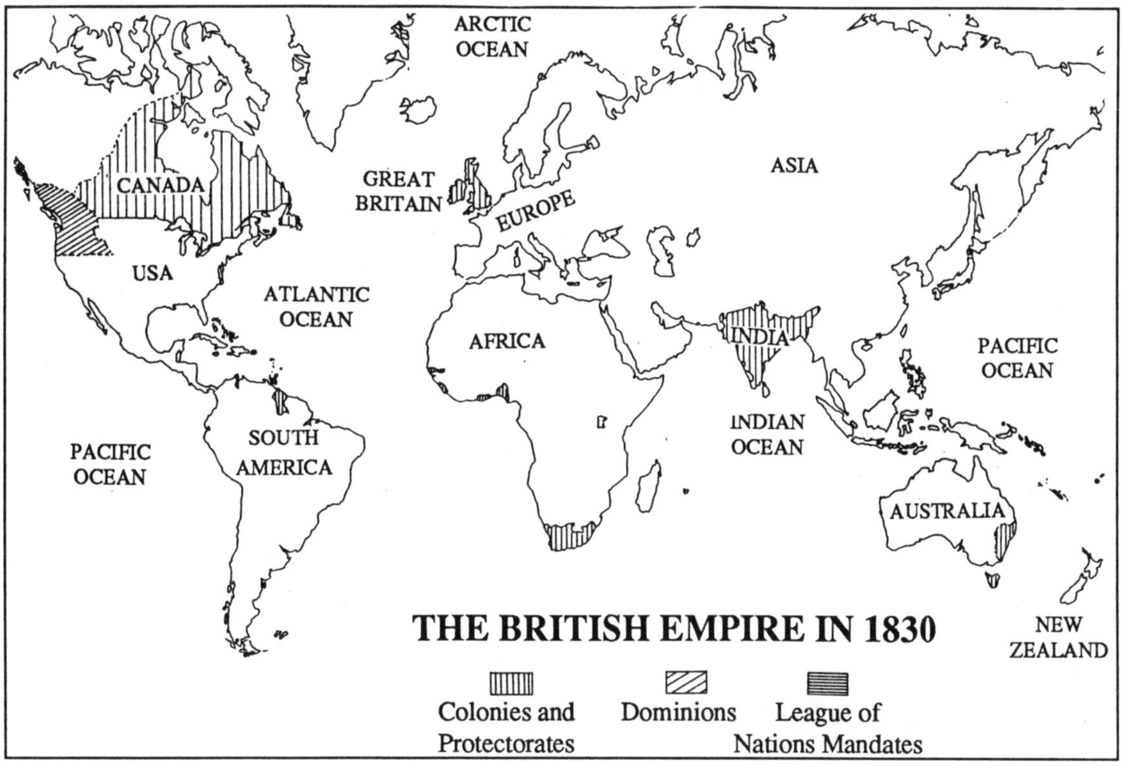

THE BRITISH EMPIRE IN 1830

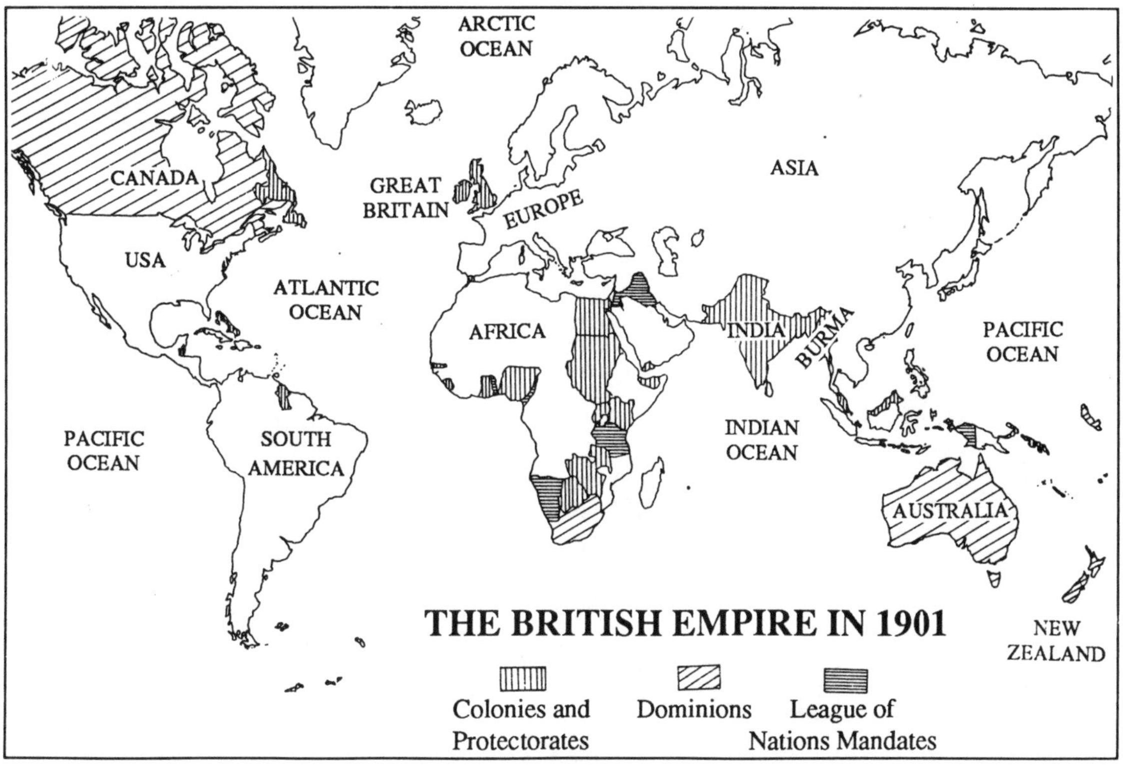

THE BRITISH EMPIRE IN 1901

The children should know what the British Empire was, how it originated and how it developed. They should know why it was important to Britain and the role of this country as its head. The meanings of colony, protectorate, dominion and the League of Nations should be explained. The children should be aware of the equivalent organisations today and how the role of Britain has changed.

BRITAIN
THE WORKSHOP OF THE WORLD

In the 19th. century, Britain had become world leader in exports and trade. To discover the roots of this prosperity it is necessary to examine the policies vis à vis trade in the 17th. and 18th. centuries.

The accumulation of capital in the 17th. and 18th. centuries was critical to economic development. During this time, home trade was nurtured by bounties and protected from foreign competition by duties on imports. The policy of protectionism including the fact that goods brought to Britain in foreign ships were subject to special taxes meant that as early as 1700, Britain had virtually destroyed Holland's monopoly for carrying the world's trade on its ships.

War and diplomacy were other factors in promoting British trade. The Methuen Treaty of 1703 aided trade with Portugal, the right of Asiento and the links with America (even after the War of American Independence, 1776 - 83) meant that trade expanded and by the end of the 18th. century trade links were well established with West Africa, America, Spanish America and the West Indies.

Another factor in Britain's prosperity was the revenue from the slave trade. Slaves were needed by farmers of the West Indies and the Southern States of America as the colonies grew: the number of slaves reached 70,000 annually by the 1780s, half of them carried on British ships.

Internally, there were other reasons for Britain's export success. These stemmed from the improvements in river transport, the building of canals, the improvements in roads (by General Wade, John Metcalf, Thomas Telford and John Loudon Macadam) and the coming of the railways. These combined to make the transport of goods a viable proposition.

By the beginning of Victoria's reign, a series of inventions and discoveries had transformed Britain's manufacturing industries. New methods of production heralded the factory system. The most important technological changes involved the harnessing of steam in industry. Improvements in blast furnace techniques such as the use of coke and then coal in smelting iron ore, the greater use of coal in producing heat and energy, the introduction of improved and sophisticated machinery, the availability of cheap labour, and the large-scale manufacture of acids, alkalis and dyes revolutionised the cotton, iron, engineering and chemical industries. Areas came to specialise in producing particular goods as local skills and resources were developed. Newcastle had shipyards and ironworks, Sheffield produced cutlery, Birmingham produced all types of metal goods, South-West Lancashire produced glass and cottons, and North Staffordshire became famous for its pottery. The major coalfields began production, tin and copper were mined in Cornwall and lead in Cumberland, West Durham and Derbyshire. Clay, slate and stone were quarried in many areas and lesser industries manufacturing silk, lace, paper and leather goods were established. The greatest industry of all, the woollen industry, grew in many areas with the south western counties, East Anglia and the West Riding of Yorkshire the main manufacturing areas.

Foreign trade developed further during the 19th. century. Britain traded with the Spanish Empire in Central and South America while the growing American colonies were eager for British goods. Tropical and sub-tropical products such as sugar from the West Indies, spices from India and the Far East, rice and tobacco from the southern colonies of America were also in demand. These were imported cheaply by British merchants in bulk then packaged and re-exported to Europe and other eager buyers at a profit.

Two other important factors which helped Britain become the 'workshop of the world' were the growth in population (aided by good harvests and a cheap and plentiful supply of food in the 18th. century) and a period of peace.

Explain to the children what the phrase the 'workshop of the world' means. Britain was not a land of large-scale industry and many people still earned part of their livelihood from agriculture. Many industries were still domestic and much work was still done in workers' homes. Words like *capitalist, entrepreneur, mechanisation, industrialisation* and *mass-production* need careful consideration. Use less difficult words such as money-provider, businessman, machines and so on. Trace the movement of the population from country to town and the implications of this. This will lead later to a discussion of the conditions in the towns. This is another situation where time-lines or diagrams can be used effectively. Outline the progress Britain had made between 1700 and the 1830s when Victoria's reign began. Pinpoint the difficulties caused by emerging industrialisation. The children can compare and contrast life in villages and towns in the 1830s and discuss the roles of those who provided capital or labour at this time.

THE INDUSTRIAL REVOLUTION

Historians still cannot agree when the 'Industrial Revolution' started and ended. Some trace the origins from the 1600s, some argue that it started after 1750. Some say it ended in 1830 or 1850 but others insist that it is a continuing process which is still going on today. There is no doubt, however, that new processes, new machines with steam power replacing human labour in the cotton, woollen, iron, coal and engineering industries constituted a 'revolution' in a real sense. Explain the term 'revolution' to the children emphasising the rapidity with which the changes occurred. Compare and contrast 'industrial' revolution with 'political' revolution. But explain that the Industrial Revolution did not happen 'in a flash'. Daniel Defoe described early 18th. century Britain as a country with growing trade and manufacturing ability and speedy economic growth:

**New discoveries in metals, mines, minerals; new undertakings in trade, inventions, engines, manufactures. These things open new scenes every day, and make England especially show a new and differing face in many places, on every occasion of surveying it.*

It is impossible to consider the Industrial Revolution in its entirety and once again the topic approach is best. You could consider developments in coal with the children or you could choose iron, textiles or chemical, gas or pottery industries. Alternatively, the children could find out about developments in these industries for themselves and compile a dossier entitled 'Revolution in Industry' to which all can contribute: this is the kind of project 'detective' work that children enjoy. [Don't forget local industries and local sites to visit.] Steam power was so crucial in all the industries that a breakdown of its development is given below. It is necessary to begin in the 17th. century, before Victorian times.

Steam power had been known for centuries but the development of a steam engine was slow.

1660 Marquis of Worcester invented a device in which steam power was used to operate a fountain.

1680 Denis Papin, a refugee French scientist, produced a steam engine called the 'Digesteur'. He also invented a safety valve.

1698 Thomas Savery invented a steam pump which was the first workable engine. It was designed to pump water out of Cornish tin mines. It made use of atmospheric pressure to raise water from the mine workings. These were channelled into a tank and steam pressure again used to drain the water away. Savery called his invention the "Miners' Friend". The pump had several disadvantages - it could only raise water slowly for about 6 metres (20 feet) at a time to a maximum of 30 metres (100 feet), it used large quantities of coal and it had no safety device and was liable to explode.

1709 Thomas Newcomen invented a pumping engine. More efficient than Savery's it could raise water from 15 metres (50 feet) below ground. In very deep mines, a number of pumps were used to work in unison. It replaced Savery's engine and was used extensively in Cornish tin mines and in coal mines until the beginning of the 18th. century.

1776 to 1788 James Watt, an instrument maker from Greenock in Renfrewshire, began work on a steam engine. With the help of John Roebuck and Matthew Boulton, he eventually perfected a rotary motion engine. This transformed industry and large-scale production was possible.

In 1781, Watt took out a second patent on an engine using the sun and planet motion, a device which enabled steam to drive all types of industrial machinery. Improvements and refinements to this invention came in 1782 when he made a double-acting expansive engine. Then in 1784 he added a parallel motion device and in 1788 a governor was added which regulated the speed of an engine so that it worked smoothly.

Steam power revolutionised industry which now no longer depended on water power and did not have to be located near flowing water. It was now possible to exploit other sources of energy such as coal. The demand for steam engines grew apace. They were used in flour mills, cotton mills, woollen mills, coal mines, brewing houses, in pottery production, for crushing sugar cane, mining iron ... By the beginning of the 19th. century, Boulton and Watt had sold 800 engines and throughout Victorian times the need for them grew rapidly.

The second half of the 19th. century marked a new phase of industrialisation - there was growing specialisation in production, the application of science to industry and the development of mass production techniques. Specialisation was very important in engineering - mechanical engineers, mining engineers and precision tool engineers appeared to meet the more intricate needs of an industrial age.

Children could research the inventions involved in steam power and the engineers responsible for the application of this power to industry. They can link the many developments using diagrams and adding famous names in the industrial processes. This should help them realise the importance of mechanisation and engineering to industry in the 19th. century.

*Daniel Defoe, *A Tour Through the Whole Island of Great Britain.* Everyman, preface to Vol II, p 133.

TOWNS AND INDUSTRIAL CONDITIONS IN EARLY VICTORIAN TIMES

In 1801 only about 20% of the population of Britain lived in towns. A century later (1901) this had risen to 75%. By mid century (1850) ten cities, including Manchester, Liverpool and Glasgow had populations of more than 100,000. London had almost 2,500,000. People had moved from rural areas to the towns because wages had declined in the countryside. In the towns, workers were needed urgently to operate machines in the new mills and factories.

Industrialists built houses for the new workers as near to the factories as possible. The main reason for choosing a site was that the workers should be able to walk to work. Dwellings were built quickly and cheaply. In the North of England and Scotland they were built close together 'back to back' in double rows. In some areas workers lived in hastily erected blocks of flats called tenements.

Such houses were small and overcrowded. Many families of five or more lived in a single room often sharing one bed. Cheap lodging houses took up to 20 or 30 people who slept on the floor with 12 occupying one room. Even the town cellars were full. It has been estimated that in Liverpool in 1850, there were 4,400 cellars with 40,000 people living in them.

In the towns there was no sanitation, no toilets and no clean water. Drinking water often had to be carried a mile or so to the houses. Back yards had to be used as toilets and rubbish was thrown into the streets and into open drains. Undernourished, overworked and living in these conditions meant that disease spread rapidly and people were often ill. There were outbreaks of cholera, typhoid and dysentery, diseases spread by infected water, which killed thousands. Typhus, tuberculosis and smallpox were rampant. Poverty in town centres was so bad that many turned to crime to feed themselves and their families. The Victorians had large families, ten children were common, but many died in infancy.

The conditions in town centres were mirrored in the factories, mills and mines. Many of the factories began in dilapidated sheds and buildings with dangerous machines running in cramped conditions: accidents were frequent. Ceilings were often so low that workers could not stand upright. Boys and girls were employed in coal and iron mines usually from the age of 8 or 9, some were even younger. Their work consisted of *opening and shutting air-doors, in throwing small pieces of coal or ironstone into the trams, or in handing implements to the men at work.*[1] Children spent days in these mines in the dark for they started before dawn and worked until dusk. Women worked long hours in equally bad conditions. Underground, the passages were often too small for adults to squeeze through and children were sent into these to retrieve coal. Many of these little ones were harnessed to coal tubs which they had to drag on all fours. Those working pumps often had to stand knee deep in cold water for hours on end.

Accidents were frequent, caused by inadequate ventilation and drainage, by entrusting 'safety' work to very young children (who sometimes fell asleep) and by falls of rock or coal. Mining was unhealthy in itself for it *deteriorates the physical constitution: the limbs become distorted: and in general the muscular power gives way* ... {Mines Report, 1842].

Elsewhere, the conditions were equally disturbing and cruelty to women and children was widespread. Richard Ostler writing in 1830 commented, *Well, I have always thought myself disgraced by being the owner of black slaves, but we never, in the West Indies, thought it was possible for any human to be so cruel as to require a child of 9 years old to work twelve and a half hours a day: and that you acknowledge is your regular practice*[2]. Boys and girls of 4, 6 and 7 were employed in most industries and in London sweated labour was generally practised: *It is not at all uncommon to find 14 to 20 children huddled together in a small room, perhaps not more than 12 feet square, and employed for 15 hours out of 24 at work that of itself is exhausting ... and is besides carried on under every possible unwholesome condition*[3].

The children should be given as clear a picture as possible of the conditions in towns and industries in the early 19th. century. Documents from factory inspectors which record these conditions are useful. Also, *The Times*, the magazine *Punch* and the writings of Charles Dickens reflect the situation amongst the working classes. Compare and contrast working conditions in 1830 with those in 1901. From then you could go further and highlight the changes up to the mid 20th. century. Point out that not all industrialists were mean, money-grasping men. Some like Cadbury in England and David Davies of Llandinam in Wales were concerned about

[1] Seymour Tremenheere's description of the mining village of Merthyr Tydfil in 1839 in a report to the Committee of the Council for Education, Appendix II: Parliamentary Papers 1840/XL, p 212.

[2] Richard Oastler, *Yorkshire Slavery in a Report on the Bill to Regulate the Labour of Children in Mills and Factories*, 1832.

[3] Children's Employment Commission, 1864

their workers. Compare and contrast the factory rules of the 1840s with the factory rules of the early 20th. century. Compare a copy of a typical factory notice of the 1840s with one in 1901. On a map (or maps) of Great Britain pinpoint the main industrial areas and note what was manufactured where and when. Consider the location of 19th. century industries and discuss why they grew up where they did. Show how towns and cities flourished where industries flourished. Draw a diagram or series of diagrams to show the growth of a town or city from a small hamlet or village. Sometimes, the work has been done for you in a local museum where you can take your children to see how your town or city has developed. Make sure the children understand the meanings of Victorian town and industrial conditions, e.g. back to back houses, no running water, no toilets, no electricity, narrow streets, no playing grounds, little time away from work ...

A time-line about progress in dealing with factory reform, the use of women and child labour may be useful to you. Note the dual affect of social action and the growth of education - as the children left industry they joined the schools.

1802 First Factory Act passed by the elder Peel limiting the working hours of workhouse children in mills to 12 hours a day for 6 days a week.

1819 Peel initiated an Act forbidding the employment of children under 9 in cotton mills and limiting the daily working hours of children between 9 - 16 to 12 hours.

1833 Lord Shaftesbury's Factory Act further raised the age of employment of children and 'young persons' and further limited their hours of work. Government inspectors were appointed. Children were to receive school instruction for two hours daily but no money was provided for this and little was done about it except where good employers provided teaching at their own expense.

1844 Sir Robert Peel's Act made a number of improvements in the existing laws.

1845 This prohibited night work in textile factories for boys and girls under 13.

1847 - 1891 Several acts attempted to control hours of work and improve working conditions including heating, ventilation, sanitation and provided for inspection by local authorities. Employers were required to tell workers of rates of pay for piece-work and to keep lists of their outworkers. This was an attempt to check 'sweated labour'.

DEVELOPMENTS IN TRANSPORT IN VICTORIAN TIMES

Before considering the developments in transport in Victorian times, consider what improvements had already been made in the 17th. and 18th. centuries. First, there had been improvements in transportation by sea and river. Rivers had been improved by eliminating meanders and replacing shallows by 'pound' locks. Bridges had replaced fords and towpaths had been built so that horse transport could be used to pull barges. Secondly, the canals of the 18th. century had further improved water transport. These had given Britain the most efficient transport it had ever known. 3,700 kilometres (2,300 miles) of canals had been built and by the early 19th. century these were carrying all kinds of merchandise.

The main changes in transport in Victorian times concerned the roads, railways, motor vehicles and ships.

ROADS

In 1700 roads were typically dirt tracks, full of ruts and potholes. Most were so narrow that there was barely enough room for one cart and passing another was impossible. Covered wagons pulled by a team of horses battled against tremendous odds and often merchants resorted to using packhorses. Thieves and vagabonds often attacked goods in transit and highwaymen robbed travellers in the dark. Maintenance was unusual, the parish being responsible for their upkeep. The road builders changed this situation. The first of these was General Wade (1668 - 1748), a professional soldier who built over 300 kilometres (200 miles) of roads in the Scottish Higlands and made them accessible. Next came John Metcalfe (1717 - 1810), nicknamed 'Blind Jack of Knaresborough' who built roads in Yorkshire, Lancashire, Cheshire and Derbyshire. He was an expert in laying good roads over boggy ground and in dealing with drainage problems. The Scot, Thomas Telford (1757 - 1834), was a great civil engineer. He built over 1,400 kilometres (900 miles) of road in Scotland and the London to Holyhead road which was the finest road in the coaching era. The last of the great road builders was John Loudon Macadam (1756 - 1836) another Scot who not only built new roads but was responsible for macadamized roads (tarmac) which made it easier and cheaper to repair them.

Throughout the 18th. and 19th. centuries turnpike trusts were set up. These consisted of groups of men permitted to put gates across sections of certain roads and charge travellers for using them. A General Turnpike Act was passed in 1773. By 1830 over 2,000 turnpike trust acts had been passed and 35,000 kilometres (22,000 miles) of roads were in the hands of trustees. [Still, 160,000 kilometres (100,000 miles) of road remained parish responsibility and were still in a shocking state of repair.] Turnpike Trusts were very unpopular in some areas. Many gates were destroyed and there was a serious riot at Bedminster in 1749. Almost a century later, the Rebecca Riots took place in Wales (1830 - 43) as protests against paying tolls to the trusts to use the roads. In the 1830s the government established Road Boards. These gradually took over management of the trusts, lowered the tolls and removed many of the gates. The trusts began to disappear and whilst there were 854 in 1871, by 1890 there were only two left. The Highways and Locomotives (Amendment) Act meant that counties were made responsible for paying half the cost of maintaining main roads. Further Acts made county councils and county borough councils responsible for all roads.

These road improvements meant that in the 19th. century, traffic increased in volume. Stage coach firms grew apace and beween 1815 - 1835 they used 3,000 coaches. Coaches were now faster and could average 16 kilometres (10 miles) per hour. Other means of road transport evolved, for example, the steam carriage and by 1833 such vehicles were operating between Cheltenham and Gloucester and London and Brighton. By 1864, their speed had reached 48 kph (30 mph) and they would have developed even further if the 'Man and Flag' Act of 1865 had not restricted their use. One invention heralded the demise of the stage coach business, the mechanical fire-horse. The age of the train had arrived.

RAILWAYS

We have seen earlier the importance of steam in industry. By the early 19th century there were several inventors trying to develop successful steam vehicles. In 1804, Richard Trevithick, a Cornish tin-mining engineer who had worked on high pressure steam engines for some years, constructed a relatively small, high pressure locomotive which people nicknamed the *Iron Horse*. His engine succeeded in hauling a load of bar iron from Penydarren to Navigation (now called Abercynon) a distance of 9 miles. With ten tons of iron and 70 people aboard, the journey took 4 hours, 5 minutes. Trevithick is regarded as the father of the locomotive and his *New Castle* engine was the first in the world to do actual work. Previously, he had built and run a steam road engine known locally as *Captain Dick's Puffer*. In 1808, he took his new 8 ton locomotive to London. He put it to work on a circular track of iron rails in an enclosure near Euston Road. He charged the public a shilling to watch or ride in a converted horse carriage pulled by his locomotive and they chugged around the

track happily at a speed of up to 12 mph. The engine was called *Catch-Me-Who-Can* and thousands took the trip until a rail snapped and the locomotive overturned.

Trevithick was a true innovator of rail for he pioneered the use of high pressure steam, the turning of the exhaust steam into the chimney to improve the draught in the fire-box, and the return flue boiler. He was also the first to show that smooth wheels could haul a load on a smooth track.

The first commercial locomotive was built by Matthew Murray for John Blenkinsop, an inspector at the Middleton Colliery near Leeds (1812). Blenkinsop insisted that it should run on the track of cast iron rails that he invented which meant that the driving wheels were fitted with a cog that slotted into toothed track. Three further locomotives were built in 1812 and 1813 and used between Middleton Colliery and Leeds, a distance of three and a half miles.

In 1813, Christopher Blackett and William Hedley built *Puffing Billy,* a simple adhesion locomotive (that is one that relied on friction between the wheels and rail and did not use the toothed rack rail system). It was used for hauling coal trucks between Wylam Colliery and the docks at Lemington-on-Tyne, a distance of about 5 miles. This locomotive can now be seen in the Science Museum in London and is the oldest steam locomotive in existence.

Men such as Trevithick, Murray, Blenkinsop, Blackett and Hedley inspired George Stephenson and his son, Robert, the most famous of the early pioneers. George was the son of a Northumberland fireman and was largely self-taught. He was appointed enginewright at Killingworth Colliery and in 1814 completed his first engine, *Blucher,* which was used to haul coal. In 1823 Stephenson was invited to build and equip a railway from Stockton to Darlington.

For the inauguration of the railway on 27th. September, 1825, George and Robert built the 4 wheeled, 8 ton engine named *Locomotion.* The 90 ton train reached a speed of 15 mph but the colliery owners were still afraid of the new phenomenon. They continued to use horses for public transport and locomotives only for coal. Nevertheless, this was the first public railway in the world intended to carry freight and passengers. *Locomotion* has been preserved and can be seen at the Darlington Bank Top Station. A replica was made and steamed for the 150th. anniversary of the railway in 1975. These locomotives were suitable only for hauling low-speed mineral trains and were limited mainly by the weak track available. At times, most of the early railways resorted to horses but the situation improved in 1827 with the introduction of Timothy Hackworth's *Royal George,* a 6-coupled locomotive. From now on the use of horses declined.

After a survey of the locomotives in existence, the directors of a new railway line undergoing construction - the Liverpool and Manchester Railway - decided to run a competition to find the best engine which met certain specified conditions which they laid out in a prospectus. The prize of £500 was to be given to the victor. Five machines were ready for the competition, the Rainhill Trials, when it began on 6th. October, 1829. The five machines were

1. *Perseverance* by Timothy Burstall,
2. *Cycloped* by Timothy Burstall,
3. *Sans Pareil* by Timothy Hackworth,
4. *Novelty* by John Braithwaite and John Ericcson and
5. *Rocket* by George and Robert Stephenson.

Locomotives were limited to those under 6 tons in weight and they were to compete on a one and a half mile track until they had travelled the same distance as a return trip between Manchester and Liverpool. *Perseverance* and *Cycloped* failed to reach the required speed limit of 10 mph and were disqualified. So was *Sans Pareil* which was over the weight limit. This left only two, *Rocket* and *Novelty.* The latter was the favourite and achieved speeds of over 30 mph. But it broke down frequently. The *Rocket* on the other hand, covered the 70 miles without a fault at an average speed of 15 mph (although it reached a speed of 29 mph occasionally). George Stephenson received the £500 and locomotives were in business. On 15th. September, 1839, the railway age began with the opening of the Liverpool and Manchester line by the Duke of Wellington. This was the first modern public railway to provide steam-hauled trains for people.

With the building of better docks in Cardiff by the Marquis of Bute, a railway link between Merthyr and the capital was needed urgently. Josiah John Guest and Anthony Hill, both from Dowlais, commissioned a young engineer named Isambard Kingdom Brunel to build such a railway. It was to be the famous Taff Vale Railway. Set up in 1836 its motto was *Cymru a fu a Chymru a fydd (Wales hath been and Wales shall be).* The first stage, Cardiff to Abercynon, was opened in 1840. 9 months later on 12th. April, 1841 the line reached Merthyr and the Taff Vale was operating.

Between 1844 - 1846, Parliament authorised the construction of over 400 railways throughout Britain. Railway 'mania' had begun in earnest. Even Queen Victoria had a train and carriage especially built for her use.

MOTOR VEHICLES

By the 1880s the technological possibilities of steam power had been fully investigated. The potential of another form of energy - the internal combustion engine - was just about to be exploited. The inventors were foreigners.

1. A Frenchman, Etienne Lenoir, produced the first practical internal combustion engine fired by gas and air (1854). Soon afterwards in 1863, he designed a self-propelled carriage which reached speeds of 8 kph (5 mph). It was a two-stroke engine but was very noisy and used large amounts of fuel.

2. Another Frenchman, Beau de Rochas, invented the four-stroke engine which was much smoother than the two-stroke (1862).

3. In 1876 a German, Nikolaus Otto, built the first commercially effective gas engine called the *Silent Otto.*

4. Two of Otto's assistants, Carl Benz (1844 - 1929) and Gottlieb Daimler (1834 - 1900) substituted petroleum for gas as fuel and the internal combustion engine became a practical possibility. In 1884 they both built petrol-driven *horseless carriages.*

There was more enthusiasm for the horseless carriage in Europe and the USA than in Britain. Indeed, development here was hampered by the Red Flag Act of 1865 which limited speeds to a maximum of 6 kph (4 mph) and had the additional proviso that such vehicles should be preceded by a man carrying a red flag to warn other road users of their potential danger. It was not until 1896 that the Act was replaced by another which raised the speed limit to 23 kph (14 mph). The repeal meant that motor cars could develop. Handmade, open to the British weather with drivers and passengers wearing special clothes and goggles, at first cars could only be bought by the rich. The Prince of Wales drove a Daimler as early as 1899 but even the wealthy virtually ignored this new form of transport until after Victoria's time. The Queen thought them *disagreeable conveyances altogether* and said, *they smell, are exceedingly nasty and are very shaky.* As far as Victorian Britain was concerned, the horse still held pride of place. Within a few years, however, (1906) 20,000 cars had been built in Britain.

SHIPS

The development of steam ships took place at the same time as steam locomotives but the former caught on much more slowly. The first steamships used large amounts of coal and there were problems with refuelling. Coaling stations had to be established in places like Gibraltar, Capetown, Aden and Singapore to provide fuel for long voyages. Steamships also had competition from clippers, the fast-moving, iron-hulled sailing ships which dominated the sea routes in the 1850s and 1860s. (In particular, Clippers vied with each other in carrying the tea crop from India and Ceylon.) By the end of Victoria's reign (1901), the steam ship had replaced sail in the world's shipping lanes. The developments in the steamship 'revolution' were briefly as follows:

1. Jonathan Hull argued *a steam vessel was a ship that could carry any ship out of harbour regardless of winds* (1736).

2. John Wilkinson, a Shropshire ironmaster, launched an iron ship on the River Severn in 1787.

3. William Symington built a wooden boat driven by a Watt steam engine (1788). In 1801 he launched his *Charlotte Dundas* steamship on the Forth-Clyde Canal.

4. Henry Bell's ship the *Comet* was launched on the Clyde in 1811.

5. 1813 There were several passenger-carrying steamships between Glasgow and Greenock on the Clyde. The first passenger steamship service began between Bristol and Bath on the Avon.

6. 1816 The first steamship service between Holyhead and Dublin.

7. 1821 Regular cross-channel steamship service.

8. 1827 There were 232 British steamboats registered.

9. 1833 The Canadian vessel, the *Royal William,* made the first Atlantic steam power crossing.

10. 1838 Sirius, a steamship built in England, made the voyage from Cork to New York in 19 days. Brunel's *Great Western* paddle-driven steamship made the voyage from Bristol to New York in 15 days. In the following 8 years the same ship crossed the Atlantic 67 times.

11. 1840 Samuel Cunard signed a contract with the government to carry the mail between England and North America. His company called at first *The British and North American Royal Steam Packets* became the famous *Cunard Line.*

12. Brunel's *Great Britain,* a ship made entirely of iron, was the first such ship to cross the Atltantic. Isambard Kingdom Brunel was one of the most outstanding of British engineers.

13. 1860 - 80 The main period of iron ship building. Brunel built the *Great Eastern* which was five times larger than any ship afloat. She carried 4,000 passengers across the Atlantic at 14 knots on her maiden voyage.

After 1850, technical developments improved ships still further. The paddle wheel was replaced by the screw which remained under water, (in stormy weather one of the two paddle wheels on a ship was usually out of the water). The tubular boiler (1848) and steel boiler (1856) were other innovations. In 1854 John Elder invented a compound marine engine requiring only a third of the fuel used by a simple steam engine. Later, the triple expansion marine engine was introduced. Finally, the steam turbine engine was developed in 1884 by Sir Charles Parsons. In this a jet of steam was directed on to rotor blades. Ten years later the turbine was used in ships and at the Spithead Review celebrating Queen Victoria's Diamond Jubilee (1897), Parsons demonstrated the speed and versatility of his vessel the *Turbinia.* It cruised at 34 knots between the battleships and the destroyer sent to intercept could not catch her. From then on the Royal Navy adopted the turbine. Steam had replaced sail. Some comparative figures are:

Year	**Sail**	**Steam**
1860	80%	20%
1880	30%	70%
1900	10%	90%

Consider the developments in transport with the children. Outline the achievements before the Victorian period, especially the importance of rivers, canals and turnpike trusts. Discuss roads in some detail: compare and contrast early Victorian roads with late Victorian roads and roads today. Investigate with the children how roads were made and how they are constructed today. Include the pioneers of the first roads. Give individual talks and projects on the great roadbuilders and mention the Scottish influence in building English roads. Explain Turnpike Trusts and how the great road builders often worked for these. Outline the opposition to these trusts. Draw a graph of road building noting that more roads were built as the 19th. century progressed. Consider the effects of good roads on transport and trade and especially on the location of industry: how the move from canals and rivers to roads influenced the location of industry. Discuss the work of navvies involved in building canals, roads and railways.

The importance of steam power can be highlighted again in the discussion about railways. Consider steam trains in relation to first the transport of raw materials, then goods and then people. Pinpoint the work of the railway engineers and the work of the navvies and illustrate the problems of building a rail network in mountainous areas. Discuss railway features including tunnels, viaducts, cuttings and embankments. Devise a railway building game to play with the children. Illustrate the Victorian attitude to railways. Discuss the social implications of the railways, for example, annual holidays for the people and the beginning of tourism. Compare and contrast the prices on railways in the 19th. and 20th. centuries. Transport policy and attitudes to railways have changed - illustrate this with reference to 19th. and 20th. centuries. Discuss and compare the problems of building new railway lines today (e.g. the line from the Channel Tunnel). Collect pictures of old trains, especially steam trains and compare the first ones with later trains. Steam trains were fascinating and today many are preserved by 'volunteers'. If possible take the children to see and ride on one of these preserved railways. A wall chart with 'Trains Past and Present' is easily put together and there are many magazines which the children can cut up and use in displays. Let the children draw and colour such famous engines as *The Flying Scotsman.* Compare and contrast modern engines with steam ones bringing them up to date with a short discussion on the latest developments in the Channel Tunnel.

Illustrate the Victorian attitude to the arrival of the motor car and take Queen Victoria's comments as typical. Show that the motor car had not really 'arrived' by the end of the 19th. century. Compare horse-drawn transport

and the car. Discuss the origin of the word 'car' from 'horseless carriage'. (The children are likely to think of others such as bus, phone . . .) Let the children investigate the lives and achievements of the motor car pioneers. Old photographs of Victorian London will show the proportion of cars to horses. Compare and contrast Victorian car adverts with motor car adverts today. Also compare and contrast Victorian cars with those today under typical headings. (Below are a few examples.)

Victorian Cars	Cars Today
Open topped	Closed
Handmade	Mass produced
Users wore special clothes	No special clothes needed
Slow speeds	Fast
Regarded as a nuisance	Regarded as a necessity
Solid tyres	Pneumatic tyres
Uncomfortable	Comfortable
Difficult to start - manual starting handles	Easy to start - batteries
Difficult to stop	Effective brakes

Let the children collect pictures of old and new cars - old cigarette cards featuring cars may be useful. A visit to a car museum is worthwhile and there are many throughout the UK. Motor car racing and drivers make interesting project subjects. A motor-car timeline compiled and illustrated by the class makes a good display.

Mention the disadvantages of the expansion of the use of cars - congestion of roads and towns, the loss of human life in accidents, the destruction of the countryside as new roads are built, pollution and its effects on the environment and health ... The growth in cars is shown by the following figures.

Year	Number of cars licensed
1906	8,500
1920	187,000
1930	Over a million
1950	2.25 million
1960	5.5 million

Steamships made of iron and steel should be discussed along with the changes in power for such vessels. Consider the advantages of iron and steel instead of wood.

1. Less danger of fire.
2. Replacement of 305 mm (12 inch) thick oak hulls by 13 mm (half inch) iron plates meant weight was reduced by a third.
3. More cargo space.
4. Steel lighter still.

Consider the dual use of ships in peace and war. Consider special vessels such as submarines and aircraft carriers. Discuss early disasters especially after the Victorian era, for example, the loss of the *Titantic*. Illustrate the negative attitude to early steamships by referring to the history and show how once people changed their minds there was a boom.

Outline the dangers of travelling by ships and illustrate by reference to RoRo ferries. Discuss how these could be made safer and the economic implications.

Time-lines for all these transport developments are useful. A transport time-line will bring all the different modes together. Comparisons are important, both contemporaneous and then and now. Where possible discuss the social and economic effects of developments and if appropriate the political influences.

THE HEALTH OF THE PEOPLE

MEDICAL ADVANCES

At the beginning of the 19th. century, there was little medical treatment for even minor illnesses. Cholera, typhus, tuberculosis and especially smallpox were endemic and even minor ailments such as the common cold were often fatal. Infant mortality from such illnesses as measles was high. The relationship between dirt and disease was not properly understood, surgery was dangerous and limited until anaesthetics were discovered. Those undergoing surgery were likely to die from shock or blood poisoning. Progress in medicine was hampered by:

1. Views of traditionalists - diseases were due to impurities in the blood and should be treated by bleeding, induced vomiting, purging or sweating. Human disorders were caused by the undertension or overtension of certain organs and should be treated by stimulation or relaxation using alcohol or opiates.

2. Diseases were not classified.

3. Dissection of human bodies was against the law.

4. Public opinion disapproved of dissection. It was contrary to popular and religious beliefs.

5. The medical profession was divided into three groups (physicians, surgeons and apothecaries)who often disagreed with each other.
   Physicians often prescribed without seeing the patient.
   Surgeons could only operate on patients externally and were not allowed to prescribe internal medicines.
   Apothecaries merely mixed drugs.

6. The relationship between dirt and disease was not known or understood.

7. There was no hygiene in hospitals.

8. Gangrene often set in when operations were performed.

9. Surgical instruments were not sterilized. Surgeons did not 'scrub-up' for operations. Often their coats were stiff with blood - the more senior the surgeon, the dirtier the coat. Doctors went from the morgue to examine women in labour and were responsible for many deaths after childbirth.

10. Little was known about diseases such as the way in which they were transmitted or how they should be treated. Scientific method and controlled experiments were often discouraged or not approved of.

Medical changes and improvements included the following:

1. New hospitals were founded. Westiminster 1719, St. George's 1733, St. Bartholomew's 1729, Guy's 1721.

2. Scientific enquiry and investigations began.
   John Hunter (1728 - 93) pioneered anatomical research.
   William Smellie improved the training of doctors and midwives.
   Edward Jenner (1749 - 1823) discovered vaccination for smallpox using a serum from cowpox. This was much safer than inoculation using the smallpox agent itself.

3. Many diseases were classified in France in the early 19th. century. This made treatment feasible. Laennec invented the stethoscope (1819) and Bequerel and Breschet popularised the clinical thermometer (1835).

4. 1800 Sir Humphrey Davy discovered nitrous oxide (laughing gas) could kill pain.
   1818 Michael Faraday discovered ether could kill pain.
   James Simpson (1811 - 70), a Scottish surgeon used chloroform as an anaesthetic.

5. Joseph Lister (1827 - 1912) proved the value of antiseptics in surgery.

6. Louis Pasteur, a French chemist and physicist, and Robert Koch, a German doctor, developed the science of bacteriology. Pasteur pioneered immunization.

7. 1895 The German physicist, Röntgen, discovered X rays which became important in diagnosis and treatment.

[Medical advances continue apace throughout the 20th century such as vitamins 1911, insulin 1922, penicillin 1928, sulphonamides 1935 - new drugs, new techniques (e.g. keyhole surgery), and new sciences such as genetics ...]

SOCIAL CHANGES

As prosperity in Victorian times and the standard of living rose, the health of the nation improved. The hours of work were reduced, housing standards and living conditions were improved by parliamentary legislation and people had more time for recreation and holidays. The availability of cheap cotton clothes, cheap soap, better food and running water were all factors in these social changes. The railway made travel to different parts of the country possible, especially days out at the seaside. The bicycle and later the motor car continued the trend. Opening children's clinics, medical inspection of children at school which began in 1907 helped to promote social awareness and reduce infant mortality. [Also see sections on class and education.]

PUBLIC HEALTH REFORM

The beginnings of reform can be traced back to the end of the 18th. century. Westminster and Portsmouth were paved and drained by 1770 and watering spas such as Harrogate, Weymouth, Bath and Brighton were well known for their cleanliness and amenities. Elsewhere, there were problems exacerbated by the number of people moving to the towns. Generally, supplies of drinking water were inadequate, the water was impure and there was little sanitation or drainage. There was no town planning and factories and houses were built higgledy-piggledy. Such conditions were highlighted by many 'reports' throughout the century.

Report of the Committee on the Health of Towns 1840. Description of Conditions in Manchester by John Robertson, A Surgeon.

Manchester has no Building Act, and hence ... each proprietor builds as he pleases. New cottages, with or without cellars, huddled together row behind row may be seen springing up ... A cottage row may be badly drained, the streets may be full of pits, brimful of stagnant water, the receptacle of dead cats and dogs, yet no one may find fault ...

J.R. Martin's Report, Parliamentary Papers, 1845.

I believe that nowhere else shall we find so large a mass of inhabitants crowded into courts, alleys and lanes, as in Nottingham. The courts are almost always approached through a low arched tunnel of some 30 to 36 inches wide, about 8 feet high and from 20 to 30 feet long They are unprovided with adequate means for the removal of refuse, ill-ventilated with a gutter, or surface drain running down the centre; they have no back yards, and the privies are common to the whole court. In all these confined quarters too, the refuse is allowed to accumulate until, by its mass and its advanced putrefaction, it shall have acquired value as manure; and thus it is sold and carted away by the 'muck majors', as the collectors of manure are called in Nottingham.

Some of the stages in public health reform.

1842 Edwin Chadwick's report on *The Sanitary Condition of the Labouring Classes* which showed the problems that existed and what should be done about them.

1848 A bad outbreak of cholera led to the Public Health Act which set up a General Board of Health. Under this, Local Boards of Health could be established. These Boards had power to borrow to finance sanitary improvements.

1858 The functions of the General Board was taken over by the Privy Council and Home Office.

1868 Torrens Act enabled local authorities to compel owners of slums to make repairs.

1875 Public Health Act compelled landlords to conform to certain standards of sanitation. Every local council had to appoint a medical officer of health.
Sale of Food and Drugs Act passed to improve the standards of food production. Local authorities could appoint food analysts and prosecute those producing adulterated food.
Artisan's Dwelling Act gave local authorities the power to demolish slums and rebuild improved houses.

The use of iron pipes for water supplies meant that water could come from distant reservoirs to supply the needs of growing towns.

Consider the health of the nation with the children. Examine with them the many problems in 1800 and how far they were solved by the end of Victoria's reign (1901). Point out which diseases were common in Britain in 1800 and how these were made worse by people living in overcrowded conditions in the new industrial towns. The class might consider, for example,

Medical problems in 1815,

Main diseases in the early 19th. century,

Why medical progress was held back in the early 19th. century.

Encourage the children to suggest possible solutions to the problems. Explain how the Victorians began to solve them. Note that many of the problems were due to the lack of education.

List some of the major discoveries and inventions in medicine in the 19th. century. Name the reformers, foreign and British, and get the children to research important lives, preferably as group work. People to concentrate on include John Hunter, Edward Jenner, Laennec, Bequerel and Breschet, Sir Humphrey Davy, Michael Faraday, Joseph Lister, Louis Pasteur, Robert Koch and Röntgen. Also consider the lives of the great reformers such as Elizabeth Blackwell, Dora Pattison, Elizabeth Garrett Anderson, Florence Nightingale, Mary Seacole and especially Sir Edwin Chadwick. Compare and contrast birth rates and death rates in early Victorian and late Victorian times and allow the children to make some deductions and inferences from this information. Discuss individual diseases that were common in Victorian times including symptoms. Discuss those which are no longer common or which are not now usually fatal (e.g. measles and scarlet fever) and the virtual disappearance of bubonic plague and the eradication of smallpox. Discuss haemophilia from which Victoria's children and other European royal families suffered.

Consider the hospitals of the early 1800s and compare them with the 1900's or today's. Consider medical opinion as far as dirt and disease were concerned, surgery then and now. Isolate the factors needed for good health and examine how these were or were not fulfilled in Victorian times. Examine the social changes and the move to public health reform. In particular, illustrate the importance of the provision of pure, clean, water for all.

CLASS AND SOCIETY IN VICTORIAN TIMES

Explain that people can be arranged into classes according to certain criteria such as

1. where they live.
2. who their parents or grandparents were.
3. their occupation.
4. their standard of education.
5. how much land and property they own.
6. how much money they have.
7. what they do in their free time.
8. how they speak, dress or behave.

The Victorians were concerned with both class and status and there were three main groups in society: the upper class, the middle class and the working class. First examine the growth of the population in the 19th. century since this has a bearing on the development of class structure.

POPULATION IN THE NINETEENTH CENTURY

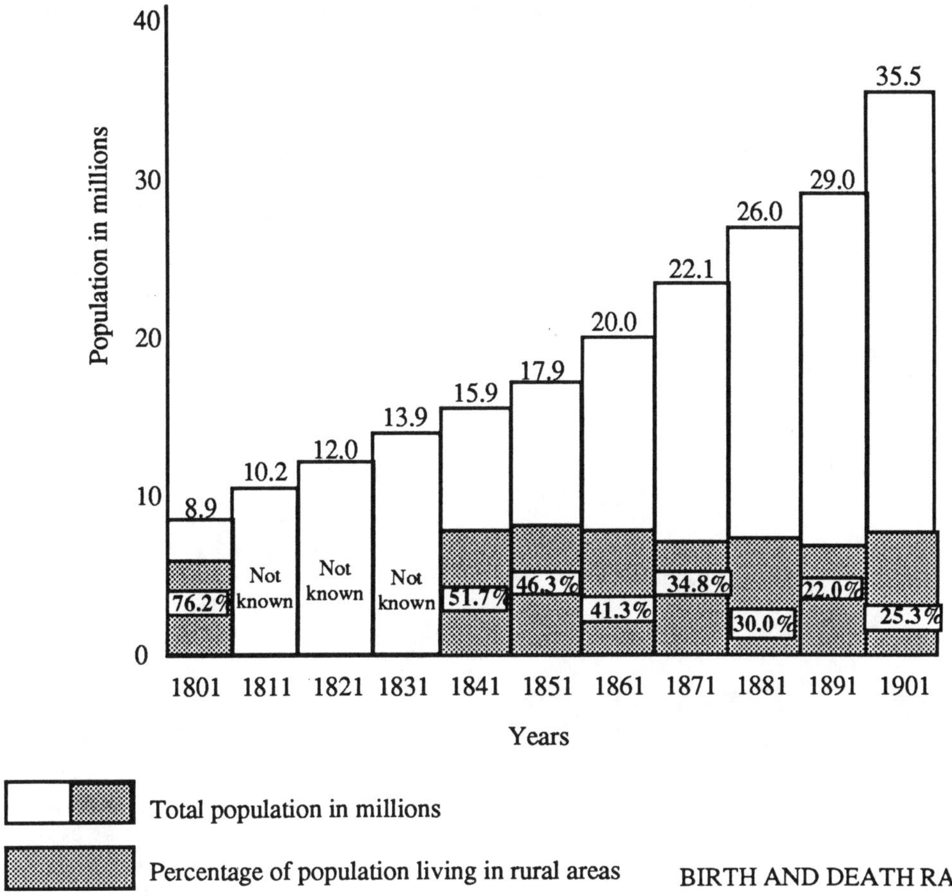

BIRTH AND DEATH RATES IN THE NINETEENTH CENTURY

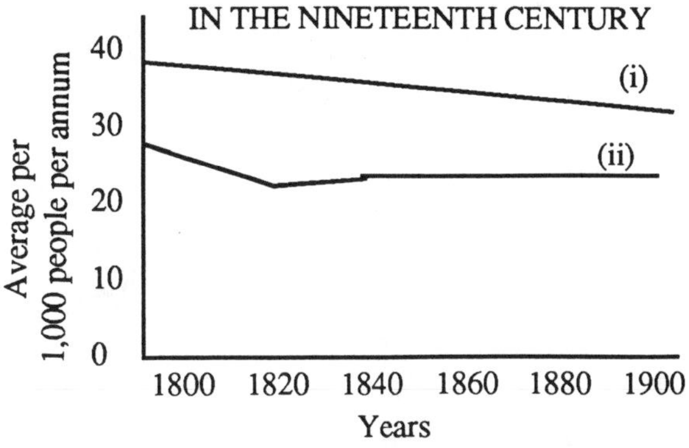

(i) Births per 1,000 people

(ii) Deaths per 1,000 people

The birth rate exceeded the death rate and the population increased from approximately 11 million in 1821 to 22 million in 1871, it had doubled in just 50 years.

THE UPPER CLASS

This class was relatively small and consisted of about 3,000 families divided into two groups, the aristocrats and the gentry.

The aristocrats were very wealthy lords and their families. They owned a great deal of land, much of which they had inherited and usually had a town house (in London) and a house or estate in the country. They had large incomes (some were over £250,000 annually) augmented by the proceeds from their land, mines and business. They did not go to work and employed servants and workers.

THE GENTRY

Usually not aristocrats, gentry owed their status to the way in which they had been educated, often at public schools. They worked for a living and had positions in the professions such as law, medicine, government, the church, the army and navy. They had incomes of at least £1,000 a year.

THE MIDDLE CLASS

This class did not do manual work. They could earn as much as £1,000 a year but many earned considerably less, sometimes as little as £150. The father was head of the household. He went out to work and the mother looked after the house and children. People who considered themselves to be middle class were usually concerned with respectability and with the way they spoke and behaved, sometimes adopting silly affectations. Many such families employed servants to do the household chores - the better off they were, the more servants they employed. As the population grew, the middle class grew with it. It was possible for a middle class family to move into the upper class, especially if they became so rich that they did not have to work.

THE WORKING CLASS

Over three-quarters of the population was considered to be working class. They were artisans, skilled workers, farm labourers, factory workers, domestic servants and those unemployed with no income.

THE EMANCIPATION OF WOMEN

Very few middle class women in the 18th. and early 19th centuries had rights or responsibilities. When a woman married all her property was transferred to her husband. *The house is his house with everything in it, and of all fixtures the most abject is his breeding machine, his wife.* (William Thompson, 1825). Women were not expected to earn their own living and the future for upper and middle class females lay in a good marriage. Paid work was infra dig and unladylike.

Working class women, on the other hand, were expected to work. First, they worked on the land, then in cottage-based industries at home and then later in mines and factories or in domestic service.

Some intelligent women pressed for more opportunities in work and education. Florence Nightingale (1820- 1910) led the way. Insisting on entering the nursing profession, she changed it out of all recognition. The idea that women could be trained for an occupation spread.

Until 1840, girls from working class families usually received no education at all. Some middle class girls went to dame schools or private schools where they learned feminine pursuits: deportment, needlework, music and dancing. In 1847, however, Mrs. Elizabeth Reid began classes for girls in her own home. In 1860 this became the first college of higher education for women in this country, namely Bedford College. Colleges providing education for women grew apace after this date [Queen's College, London 1848, Hitchin College 1869, Girton College, Cambridge 1873, Newnham College, Cambridge 1871 - 1880, Sommerville and Lady Margaret Hall, Oxford 1879].

As more women became educated they demanded entry into the professions. The first to admit them was medicine. The pioneer was Elizabeth Garrett Anderson. She studied medicine in England but was forced to take her degree in Paris. In 1874, the London School of Medicine for Women began and by 1901 there were 335 qualified women practitioners. Later, women entered the legal profession.

The invention of the telephone and typewriter meant that women began to work in offices and by 1901 retail shops also employed thousands of females. The Married Women's Property Acts of 1870, 1882 and 1893 also helped women by giving them legal control over their property.

The only male bastion left was parliamentary reform and from the 1870s, demands for votes for women became more urgent. This led eventually to numerous petitions to parliament and the suffragette movement. Women were not allowed to vote on equal terms with men until 1928, that is, women over 21 could vote.

Discuss with the children what is meant by class and the classes in Victorian society. Explain class and point out the differences between class/society then and now. Compare and contrast Victorian class structure with

20th. century class structure. Have class pressures declined? Consider a typical upper class family, a typical middle class family and a typical working class family in Victorian times. Draw a chart differentiating between the three. Discuss how belonging to a particular class affected family life. Use house signs and numbers of rooms to indicate class levels and structures. Let the children imagine they belong to one or other of the classes and write about their daily lives. Use role play to show the differences between the classes. Explain the reasons for the growth of population and how this affected the class structure of Victorian society.

Discuss what is meant by 'emancipation' and consider this in relation to prejudice. Are women completely emancipated today? What restrictions still exist? Consider the equality of women in Victorian times and today. Outline the stages in women's emancipation and allow the children to research some of the leading figures in this movement such as Elizabeth Reid, Charles Kingsley, F. D. Maurice, Frances Mary Buss, Dorothea Beale, Emily Davies, Anne Clogh, Elizabeth Garrett Anderson, Ann Knight, Lydia Becker, Eva Gore-Booth, Emmeline Pankhurst, Flora Drummond and Emily Wilding Davison.

Discuss whether the children would rather live today or in Victorian times. Their reasons are usually enlightening.

CRIME AND PUNISHMENT

Poverty in Victorian city centres led to an increase in crime. Assault and robbery were commonplace: pickpockets, swindlers and forgers plied their evil trades. Burglary and house-breaking flourished. Sir Robert Peel founded the Metropolitan Police to try to combat crime and by 1839 police forces were being set up countrywide.

Crime was severely punished. Men and women were flogged or sentenced to long terms of imprisonment. Many were hanged and others were sent to Australia. Many prisoners died in prison ships in London docks and elsewhere and others on convict ships on the way to Australia. Victorian jails were overcrowded and filthy. Many women had their children in prison with them. Conditions were indescribably bad. Elizabeth Fry helped to improve conditions and after 1840 new prisons were built. Prisoners were not allowed to speak to one another and were condemned to silence even when eating, working or exercising.

THE WORKHOUSE AND ITS RÉGIME

The Act responsible for the workhouse system was the Poor Law Amendment Act (1834). This laid down

1. that parishes should be joined to form unions: in each union poor relief was to be administered by Boards of Guardians with the Poor Law Commission supervising from London.
2. that there should be no outdoor relief for the able bodied. If such persons or families were to receive relief they must go into a workhouse.
3. that conditions inside the workhouse were to be 'less eligible' which meant that a family inside would have less attractive circumstances than the poorest outside.

The régime in these workhouses was very strict.

1. Men, women and children were separated and had to work and sleep in diferent rooms. This meant that families were not together.
2. Everyone had to wear workhouse clothes.
3. All had to obey workhouse rules.
4. Children's hair was cut short.
5. A diet was laid down consisting mainly of bread, cheese and gruel (oatmeal boiled in water). There was little variation in this diet and never enough to eat.
6. All had to work hard at menial jobs: men crushed animal bones to make fertilizer for crops or broke up stones for road building, the women had to chop wood or wash clothes in a laundry.
7. The timetable was harsh: inmates worked 10 hours a day.

TYPICAL WORKHOUSE TIMETABLE

6.00 am		Rise
6.30 - 7.00 am		Breakfast
	WORK	
12.00 am - 1.00 pm		Dinner
	WORK	
6.00 pm - 7.00 pm		Supper
8.00 pm		Bed

VICTORIAN CLOTHES

The amount of money Victorians spent on clothes depended on their incomes. Working class clothes were usually made of coarsely woven homespun wool. Work in factories made it difficult to keep clothes clean and they were often torn and dirty. Poor families could not buy shoes for their children because they were too expensive and many went without shoes. It was usual for children to wear the cast-offs of their parents or older brothers cand sisters. Girls usually wore dresses, sometimes with a pinafore, and boys wore shirts and trousers. Most people tried to keep some clothes to wear on Sunday - their 'Sunday best'. Poorer families had to make all their clothes last. Babies from poor families wore thin dresses and were often wrapped in shawls previously used by older children.

Wealthier families could afford better quality material. Men wore knee-length frock coats made of silk or velvet. These were made in plain, dark colours. They also wore silk waistcoats and had a sash around the middle. They wore shirts with stiff, high collars and ties or cravats around the neck. Trousers were not creased but fastened by a strap which went beneath the shoes. Beards and side whiskers were in fashion and most men wore or carried gloves and sticks or canes. Men's underclothes consisted of long sleeved woollen vests and long woollen underpants.

Early Victorian women wore wide skirts with flounces held out by crinolines. Small head bonnets were fashionable. By the early 1870s, skirts were now worn over bustles - padded cushions tied behind the waist under the dress which made it stick out. Narrow waists were the height of fashion. Elegant ladies wore tightly laced corsets. Some of these were pulled so tight that they restricted breathing and the wearers were in danger of fainting.

Well-off Victorian children followed the fashion of their parents. Their clothes were actually smaller versions of what Mum and Dad wore. Girls wore long skirts and smocked dresses or short dresses with stockings or pantaloons underneath. Pinafores were sometimes worn over these dresses. Girls wore vests, several petticoats and teenagers began to wear corsets.

Boys wore dresses until they were about 4 years old.Then they were given trousers (they were 'breeched'). Older boys wore shirts, jackets, knee-breeches, socks, shoes or boots and a cap or hat, usually a straw-boater. Sailor suits were fashionable because the sons of royalty wore them but so were velvet suits with lace collars and cuffs. Long curls were also in vogue. Rich babies wore vests and dresses, bootees and bonnets.

The material used for clothes included calico, cashmere, cotton, flannel, hessian, lace, muslin, silk, towelling and wool. There were, of course, no synthetics.

Discuss the clothes the Victorians wore. What is meant by fashion? Show how fashions change. Make contrasting lists of clothes worn in the period up to 1901. The headings

Material   Age Range   Male   Female   Children

are useful. Let the children compare the clothes with what is worn today. Discuss how the attitudes to clothes and fashions have changed. Explain that all clothes had to be made by hand before the industrial revolution and the invention of a practical sewing machine in 1851. Isaac Merrit Singer's invention led to the mass production of clothing which affected the ways people dressed. Discuss the effects of mass production on clothes and fashion today. Show how the coming of synthetics also caused change and note the move amongst the young to denims and jeans. Note also the speed with which fashion changes today and discuss if this would have been possible in Victorian times. Obtain pictures or photographs of what was worn. Examine these with the children and compare and contrast changes as the Victorian age progressed. Let the children see any exhibition of costume and dress in your area. There may be a period piece on television or a video available which may be helpful.

EDUCATION AND SCHOOLING IN VICTORIAN BRITAIN

At the turn of the century (1800), Joseph Lancaster confidently boasted that *a boy who can read, can teach, although he knows nothing about it.* The education that was available was not designed for all but only for a few. It can conveniently be divided into three levels: education at the universities, education for the upper and middle classes and lastly for the lower classes - the poor. As the century progressed, attention was paid to education for the poorer classes and university scholars. Middle class education was sandwiched in the middle and a gap existed which had to wait almost a century to be filled by anything like a workable system.

What education existed just before Victorian times? The universities had long been in a state of decline. In the 18th. century, scholars spent most of their time in the taverns and work stopped at dinner time, which meant 11 o'clock in 1800. Extravagance, indulgence, gambling and debt were common. Professors rarely lectured, examinations were either non-existent or prefunctory. It was to be two or three decades before reform of Oxford and Cambridge began and well after mid-century before such reforms influenced other levels of education.

There were different strata of poor people in the early part of the 19th. century. There were the healthy poor who were not particularly skilled at any work and the indigent poor who could not work even if there were jobs available. In the 1830s and 1840s, an aristocracy of the poor emerged, the skilled artisans. There had been various attempts aimed at educating these groups. **Charity Schools** had existed for centuries, and since 1699, the **Society for the Promotion of Christian Knowledge** had done its best for the healthy and indigent poor. The **dame schools,** of varying quality, also looked after scores of children by day. Many were mere baby-minding institutions and did little for the street Arabs who roamed urban areas in search of mischief and entertainment. The **Sunday School Movement** established by men like Robert Raikes to keep children out of trouble on Sundays was augmented by the **Ragged Schools** in the week. The latter were designed to give a modicum of instruction often on a part-time basis to the poorer class of children who wandered through the streets with nothing to do. **Schools of industry** were also started for those working in factories. Sir Robert Peel's Factory Act of 1802 (entitled the 'Health and Morals of Apprentices Act') was the first in a long line of measures setting up industrial trade schools. This provided that in some part of the working day, apprentices should be given some teaching in the three R's and religion. In all these schools there was a chronic lack of resources and thus Joseph Lancaster and Andrew Bell devised the monitorial system as a way of teaching the many children needing instruction.

Middle class education had a rich heritage extending back to medieval, Elizabethan and Stuart times. Besides the medieval grammar schools there were other endowed institutions. These were the **great schools** (the term public shools had not yet been invented) like the College of the Blessed Mary of Eton, Saint Mary College, Winchester, the Collegiate School of Saint Peter, Westminster and the free Grammar School of King Edward the Sixth at Shrewsbury and others like Harrow, Rugby, Charterhouse and the day schools of St. Pauls and Merchant Taylors. By 1800, the important Academies of the 17th. and 18th. centuries, strongholds of nonconformity, had largely disappeared and the schools founded by the Jesuits in the 17th. century had been brought to an end by the Revolution of 1688. Besides the endowed grammar and *great schools,* there were only the preparatory and private schools left. They were mostly inadequate and only a few like Hazelewood, Birmingham and Bruce Castle, Tottenham were of any use at all. Very shortly, however, in the new century, proprietary schools were to begin followed by the Woodard Schools, the National School and Fortescue and Brereton's County Schools.

Despite the inadequacies of the university and middle school institutions, there was little criticism of them in Victorian times. Indeed, the feeling was that the middle classes and those at university were adequately provided for: The problem uppermost in Victorian minds was the problem of educating the labouring poor. The rising birthrate meant increasing numbers of children, the new urbanisation associated with industrial and agricultural change meant that the charity schools like those run by the SPCK were unsuitable, and there was a surge of working class interest in education. Anglican and Nonconformists were soon to vie with one another as two new societies began to provide places of education for the poor. By 1820, the **National Society,** organised by the Church of England, and the **British and Foreign Society** were firmly established.

In early Victorian times there were two general views on the education of the poor. The first was that providing them with education was likely to generate disaffection. Mr. Davies Giddy, Member of Parliament, argued that education would enable the poor to read seditious pamphlets, vicious books and publications against Christianity. Dr. James Kay, destined to be the first secretary of the Committee of Council for Education in 1839, warned that *educating the poor would be like putting the torch of knowledge into the hands of rick burners* and Andrew Bell argued it would be *unwise to elevate by education the minds of those doomed to drudgery.* The general view was that society had been stratified from time immemorial and should remain

so: each man should know his place in the class system.

The second view was that education should be an agent of social control. Adam Smith argued that a well informed public was more decent and orderly than an illiterate one and Hannah More, the Evangelical educationist who was responsible for organising Sunday schools in the Mendips, subscribed to the view that education could be so organised and controlled that there would be respect for superiors and deference to God:

My plan of instruction is extremely simple and limited, she said. *They learn on week-days such course works as may fit them for servants. I allow of no writing for the poor. My object is not to make fanatics, but to train up the lower classes in habits of industry and piety. I know no way of teaching morals but by teaching principles, or of inculcating Christian principles without imparting a good knowledge of scripture.*

Educational theory was in its infancy, at least in England. One view was that the mind of a child was a blank sheet and upon this anything could be written. The only way to educate was by rote - repetition and mechanistic learning was the order of the day. There was little realisation that a child's mind, like his body, gradually grows to maturity and has to be nurtured like a young plant. (Freobel's *kindergarten* was to show how important this was some decades later.) Mechanistic learning, the reciting and memorisation of facts, was regarded as the only way to learn, the infant being regarded as a *young adult.* Another view which was prevalent was that education was so easy to impart that children could be taught *en masse* - there was no concern about the differences between individuals. The division of labour had been successful in the factory system and it was thought the *principle in schools and manufactories would be the same.* Thus, it was that the monitorial system achieved popularity and acclaim:

By a series of improvements, he [i.e. Joseph Lancaster] *at length demonstrated the possibility of instructing even a thousand cildren (if so many could be collected together in one room); by a single master; he divided his school into eight classes, each of which was managed by a monitor, whose duties were exactly prescribed to him, and was made responsible for the good order of his class: over these, a monitor-general was placed, who regulated the business of the whole school, under the immediate direction of the master.*

Little was achieved as far as legislation was concerned in the field of popular education in the first twenty-five years of the 19th. century. The new towns were places of disease and squalor and the unsanitary living conditions and the long hours worked contributed to the relentless round of human misery. Men, women and children could find employment in the new industries but it was necessary for whole families to work because the wages were so very small. Employers paid as little as they could: child labour was economically attractive to them and they fought tooth and nail to keep their young charges as little more than slaves, working for a mere pittance. Child-labour was a major obstacle to the provision of popular education and employers immediately looked for loopholes in any Factory Acts that were passed that would enable them to keep youngsters at their work.

The efforts to introduce basic educational reform in the 19th. century must be considered against this background. There were the problems associated with the end of the war in Europe: of agricultural recession and industrial expansion (both detrimental to the poorer class), the serious shortage of schools and especially schoolmasters, and the lack of any co-ordinated educational provisions. Praise must be accorded to pioneers like Lancaster and Bell, Peel and Whitbread, Brougham and Roebuck for their attempts to promote educational reform under such adverse circumstances.

It was not until 1870 that the government took a hand in education. An Act passed in that year allowed new schools to be built. It also agreed to pay teachers' salaries and allocated money to buy books and equipment, provided the schools maintained certain (minimum) standards. These new schools were called **Board Schools** because they were looked after by boards or committees of local people. The government was concerned to maintain standards and only gave a full grant to schools if the children attended regularly and did well in examinations. They were especially concerned about basic subjects like reading, writing and arithmetic. In schools where attendance was poor or the required standards were not reached, the money grants were reduced or stopped altogether. This system was known as 'payment by results'. Teachers therefore had a vested interest in school children attending and doing well.

The Board Schools lasted for the rest of Queen Victoria's reign. In 1901 she died, and a year later the Board Schools came to an end, and the government decreed that schools were to be run by local authorities.

The children will be fascinated with a comparison of the Victorian school with theirs today. Emphasize any similarities and differences. Use role play and turn your class into a Victorian place of learning. Let the children dress up if they wish and introduce Victorian schoolroom paraphernalia such as an abacus, a dunce's cap, a board duster, chalk, an old desk, an inkwell, a mortar board ... Include photographs and artefacts from Victorian days and if possible, old school regulations, notices and registers. The children can make their own costumes. Get the children to ask their families about their own schooldays and let them make comparisons. A visit to a local museum with a Victorian schoolroom can help bring the topic to life. Let the children write a story about a day in the life of a Victorian child at school. Explain the monitor system and instruct some

members to follow the example of someone you appoint as monitor.

Show how the Victorian school was regimented and why silence was important. How would they react to strict discipline including corporal punishment? Explain what the Victorians meant by drill. Let the children write on slates, count with old money, chant tables and recite poetry.

Compare the régime of the Victorian schoolroom with the openness of schools today. Let the children consider the main laws which changed education in the 19th. century and the effects of the various acts.

The children's opinions on what was taught in the Victorian schoolroom and what should be taught today are always interesting and often surprisingly 'grown up'. What changes would the children like to see today?

VICTORIAN SCHOOLROOMS

The following places have replica or reconstructed Victorian schoolrooms/classrooms/schools.

The Black Country Museum, Tipton Road, Dudley, West Midlands DY1 4SQ. Tel. 0121 557 9643.

Bliss Hill Open Air Museum, Legges Way, Madeley, Telford, Shropshire. Tel. 01952 586063/583003.

Bradford Industrial Museum, Moorside Road, Eccleshill, Bradford, West Yorkshire. Tel. 01274 631756.

Braintree District Museum, Manor Street, Braintree, Essex CM7 6YG. Tel. 01376 550066.

Katesgrove Schoolroom, Katesgrove Primary School, Dorothy Street, Reading, Berkshire. Tel. 01734 574678.

Leeds Industrial Museum, Armley Mills, Canal Road, Armley, Leeds LS12 2QF. Tel. 01532 637861.

Macclesfield Heritage Centre, Roe Street, Macclesfield, Cheshire SK11 6UT. Tel. 01625 613210.

Museum of Childhood, Sudbury Hall, Sudbury, Ashbourne, Derbyshire DE6 5HT. Tel. 01283 585305.

Museum of Childhood, Judges' Lodgings, Church Street, Lancaster LA1 1YS. Tel. 01524 846315.

The North of England Open Air Museum, Beamish, County Durham DH9 0RG. Tel. 01207 231811.

Shugborough, Milford, Stafford ST17 0XB. Tel. 01889 881388.

Ragged School Museum, 46 - 48 Copperfield Row, Bow, London E3 4RR. Tel. 0181 990 6405.

St. John's House, St. John's, Warwick CV34 4NF. Tel. 01926 412021.

Sevenoaks Museum and Gallery, Sevenoaks Library, Buckhurst Lane, Sevenoaks, Kent TN13 1LQ. Tel. 01732 453118/452384.

Sevington School, Sevington, Chippenham, Wiltshire. Tel. 01249 783070.

Tudor House Museum, Friar Street, Worcester WR1 2NA. Tel. 01905 20904.

Weald and Downland Open Air Museum, Singleton, Chichester, West Sussex PO18 0EU. Tel. 01243 63348.

Welsh Folk Museum, St. Fagans, Cardiff CF5 6XB, Tel. 01222 569441.

Wigan Pier Heritage Centre, Wigan, Lancs.WN3 4EU. Tel. 01942 323666.

RELIGION IN VICTORIAN BRITAIN

Religion was important to middle class and upper class Victorians. The Church of England or Anglican religion attracted those from the more prosperous strata of society. Church-going was fashionable and pews were padded, lined and cushioned: many had the family name on them. Church-going was an important social occasion and families wore their 'Sunday best' clothes. At home there were bible readings and prayers as part of the normal daily routine.

A census taken on 30th. March, 1851 in England and Wales showed that only half the population of about 18 million attended religious services and only about 3 million of these were Anglican. It was clear that the working classes were not attending. They believed that the Church was in league with the well-off and the landowners: they resented being second-class citizens sitting on hard seats and kneeling on cold stone. Many working class souls found succour in Nonconformism. They became Baptists, Methodists or some other denomination worshipping in chapels. These chapels became a focus for the social life of communities throughout the country.

The influence of Christianity meant that there were many who wanted to carry out social reform. William Booth, William Gladstone, George Cadbury and Thomas Barnardo were a few reformers inspired by Christianity to improve the lot of their fellow men. Others were inspired to carry the message of the gospel to countries overseas and much missionary work was undertaken in this period.

Discuss the Victorian attitude to religion with the class and explain how Anglicanism appealed to the middle and upper classes. Consider the importance of the Victorian Sunday which was sacrosanct: compare with Sundays today. Why were the working class disenchanted with church? Where did they find solace? If possible visit a Victorian church and point out evidence of Victorianism in the building and outside. Let them sketch or trace a Victorian church (inside and outside) and point out any particularly Victorian features. Explain about denominations and how churches and chapels differed inside and doctrinally. Let the children write about a typical Victorian Sunday - what was allowed and what was not. Visit a local graveyard and get the children to take notes on Victorian burials. Point out the significance of the ages of the deceased. Let the children find out the life expectancy of people in Victorian times. Compare with today and suggest reasons for the difference.

Explain what is meant by a missionary and consider the life and work of one of the great Victorian missionaries. Consider the work of one of the reformists such as William Booth who founded the Salvation Army in 1878 or Dr. Barnardo who founded homes for orphans.

WORKING CLASS MOVEMENTS AND PARLIAMENTARY REFORM

In this section we shall deal with a number of working class movements which helped to change and shape Victorian society.

THE CHARTISTS

Based mainly on economic grievances, this movement had political aims. It grew
1. out of disappointment with the Reform Act, 1832.
2. as a reaction against the failure of early Trade Unions.
3. in opposition to the new Poor Law - the 1834 Poor Law Amendment Act.
4. and out of discontent with cyclical unemployment and depression.

The Chartists led by William Lovett, Henry Hetherington and Francis Place wanted Parliament to accept and adopt the People's Charter. There were six demands.
1. Votes for all men over 21.
2. Voting by secret ballot.
3. Equal electoral districts.
4. Abolition of the property qualification for MPs.
5. Payment of MPs.
6. Annual parliaments.

Three huge petitions were submitted to Parliament in 1839, 1842 and 1848 but after 1848, the Movement faded out completely.

THE CO-OPERATIVE MOVEMENT

This was based on the idea of joint ownership of the means of production and distribution with the workers being the members. Robert Owen was one of the earliest advocates of the Movement but his early efforts failed. The Movement became successful from 1844. Then, seven weavers formed the Rochdale Society of Equitable Pioneers. With 28 members and a working capital of just £28, they established a shop in Toad Lane. The aims of the society were

The establishment of a store for the sale of provisions, clothing, etc. The building, purchasing, or erecting a number of houses, in which those members, desiring to assist each other in improving their domestic and social conditions, may reside. The manufacture of such articles as the Society may determine upon, for the employment of such members as may be without employment, or who may be suffering in consequence of repeated reductions in their wages.

From such small beginnings the Co-operative Movement grew. In 1873 the Co-operative Wholesale Society covering the whole country was founded and in 1876 the Co-operative Bank began. By 1914 the number of members was over 3 million and the financial capital was over £64 million.

TRADE UNIONS

The Combination Acts of 1799 and 1800 meant that workers and employers were not allowed to meet to regulate wages and hours of work. By the beginning of the Victorian period they were repealed, mainly as a result of the work of Francis Place a tailor from Charing Cross Road and the radical MP Joseph Hume. Trade Unions now started to grow. In 1834 a Grand National Consolidated Trades Union acquired half a million members. These organisations had grandiose plans, made impossible promises to their members such as high wages and a working day of just four hours, and they soon collapsed. Trade was depressed until 1841. As trade improved, so labour organisations again developed, this time with more sober aims. Their fundamental aim was to obtain better conditions of employment for the members and provide some form of support to enable members to withdraw their labour, that is to strike as a way of influencing employers. In 1850, the Amalgamated Society of Engineers was formed and soon it set an example of efficiency to all other unions. It limited membership to workmen who had served full legal apprenticeships, sought a uniform trade policy and kept strict control of authority to grant or refuse strike pay. It also developed provisions for sick and accident benefits, unemployment allowances and pensions for aged members. From 1857 - 58 there was a series of unsuccessful strikes during a trade slump and unions now turned to political action. Permanent Trade Councils were formed in the chief industrial towns and the first Trades Union Conference was held in London in 1864. Up to 1875 the unions helped to negotiate conditions in the work place and increase its political influence. In 1867 they secured the Master and Servant Act which removed the worst injustices of the law of

WORKING CLASS MOVEMENTS AND PARLIAMENTARY REFORM

contract between employer and workman. After the Reform Act (1867) the unions strived to increase their political influence by registering their members as electors and pressing parliamentary candidates for pledges in support of legislation for their rights. In 1873 the Gladstone Ministry passed the Trade Union Act giving some measure of legal protection to unions and their funds. It also passed a Criminal Law Amendment Act making it illegal for trade unions to coerce workers to join. This was worded so that strikers could be prosecuted on very slight grounds. The unions protested against this law and for the first time put forward Labour candidates in the election of 1874. Two were successful and they were expected to look after the interests of the unions and their members. Many Conservatives were elected by the support of the unions and Disraeli's Ministry repealed the CLA Act in 1875 and passed the Employers and Workmen Act which gave unions complete recognition, made employment a civil contract with both parties equal and abolished imprisonment for breach of contract. In the same year the Conspiracy and Protection of Property Act legalised peaceful picketing and made trade disputes exempt from the law of conspiracy. The friendly society (benefits) element developed greatly in the unions from 1852. The organisation of women workers was almost non-existent until 1872 after which a few small unions were founded. Agricultural workers were especially difficult to organise but between 1872 and 1875 about 100,000 rural workers joined their union.

New unions representing unskilled, poorly paid workers flourished after 1889. There were a number of strikes which were effective but trade unions got into difficulties in the courts for their actions against employers.

In 1900 a short strike took place on the Taff Vale Railway in South Wales and the railway company sued the union (the Amalgamated Society of Railway Servants) and was awarded £23,000 in damages. This judgement which crippled the unions was not overturned until the Victorian age was over. The Trades Disputes Act (1906) enacted that trade union funds were not liable for civil wrongs: thus if a union withdrew the labour of its members, leading to a breach of contract with the employers, the union could not be held liable for damages.

THE RISE OF THE LABOUR PARTY

The idea of socialism was to change the social and economic order in society in favour of the working classes who made up the great mass of the people. The pioneers were Karl Marx (1818 - 1883) and Friedrich Engels. They wrote 'The Communist Manifesto' (1848) and Marx developed his theories of the class struggle in his book, 'Das Kapital' (1867). In his book Marx foresaw class warfare between the workers and capitalists arguing that the workers would eventually win. A classless society would then follow where the means of production, distribution and exchange would become public property. Socialism developed in many countries in Europe and Chartism appeared in Britain. This was followed in 1861 by Henry Hyndman's 'Democratic Federation' which organised demonstrations in Trafalgar Square, London. It advocated free education and the nationalization of land, railways, mines and banks.

In 1884 a group of middle class intellectuals including Sydney and Beatrice Webb and the playwright George Bernard Shaw founded the Fabian Society. They advocated achieving socialism *through the inevitability of gradualness.*

William Morris in *Useful Work and Useful Toil* attacked low wages in 1885:

> *The 'manufacturer' aims primarily at producing, by means of the labour he has stolen from others, not goods but 'profit', that is the 'wealth' that is produced over and above the livelihood of the workmen. Whether that 'wealth' is real or sham matters nothing to him. If it sells and yields him a 'profit' it is all right . . . It is this system, therefore, which we must be resolute in getting rid of, if we are to attain to happy and useful work for all. The first step towards making labour attractive is to get the means of making labour fruitful, the Capital, including the land, machinery, factories etc., into the hands of the community, to be used for the good of all alike.*

James Keir Hardie, a Scottish coalminer, is regarded as the founder of the Labour Party. In 1892 he was elected MP for West Ham and in 1893 became chairman of a conference of trade union delegates and representatives of socialist groups which met at Bradford and formed the Independent Labour Party. In the general election of 1895, however, the party did not return any of its 28 candidates to Parliament. History for the Labour Party had to wait until 1900. Then, the Labour Representation Committee was founded. Its chairman was Keir Hardie and its secretary was James Ramsay Macdonald who later became the first Labour Prime Minister.

The growth of the Labour Party astonished political observers. In 1900 two socialist MPs (Keir Hardie for Merthyr Tydfil and Richard Bell for Derby) were returned, the total Labour vote being 63,000. In 1906 the Labour vote was 323,000 and 29 Labour MPs were elected. In 1910 there were 42 Labour MPs.

PARLIAMENTARY REFORM

In the 19th. century, parliamentary reform made the House of Commons a more representative body. Here we shall briefly trace the reform of the franchise from 1832 until the early 20th. century.

Let us start with the position prior to 1832.

1. **Very few people had the right to vote.** In a population of 14 million there were hardly half a million voters (just 1 in 28 could vote.)
2. There were **many rotten boroughs,** that is places which had declined but which still sent representatives to parliament. For example, Old Sarum, near Salisbury, consisted of a ploughed field and some broken walls and two electors (or voters) who returned two members to parliament.
3. There were also a number of **pocket boroughs,** towns incorporated under ancient charters but which had very small numbers of voters, sometimes just the mayor and corporation! The state of the franchise of the whole of Scotland at this time was described by Bagehot:
   In the towns the franchise belonged to a close and self electing corporation, who were always carefully watched: the country representation, anciently resting on a property qualification, had become vested in a few titular freeholders, something like lords of the manor, only that they might have no manor; and these, even with the addition of the borough freeholders, did not amount to three thousand. The whole were in the hands of Lord Eldon's party and the entire force, influence, and patronage of government were spent to maintain and keep it so.
4. The gross **inequalities of representation.** Large, but incorporated towns such as Manchester, Birmingham, Sheffield and Bradford, had no representation while a hundred towns whose population was not equal to that of Manchester alone returned 200 members.
5. The **anomalies of qualification for a vote,** e.g. as between freeholders, leaseholders, tenants at will and other classes of occupiers.
6. The **system excluded the middle classes** from participation in the working of government and in the shaping of public policy. It gave landowners far too much influence in the House of Commons.

THE REFORM ACT OF 1832 This took away 143 seats from 'rotten' and 'pocket' boroughs and transferred them to large and hitherto unrepresented towns and to the counties. The county seats were increased from 94 to 159. Scotland received 8 more seats and Ireland 5. In the boroughs the old and complicated forms of qualification were abolished. A uniform franchise was established for all adult male householders who paid an annual rent of £10 or more. In the counties the vote was extended to possessors of a 40s freehold and and then to £10 copyholders and those who paid £50 upwards rent for houses or land. Briefly, the Act enfranchised the moneyed commercial and middle classes and larger farmers (if you were male). It reduced the political power of the landowners. It enfranchised nearly half a million new voters, making the total electorate almost a million (1 in 14 of the population could vote.) The limited extent of this reform is shown by considering Manchester. It had a population of 185,000 and just 4,200 persons on its register of voters.

THE SECOND REFORM ACT OF 1867 This increased the number of people who were eligible to vote but the conditions were still based on owning property or paying rent or rates and still applied only to men. In English and Scottish boroughs, adult male householders who had been resident for a year and had paid poor-rates, and lodgers with a year's residence who paid a rent of £10 or more for unfurnished rooms were now permitted to vote. In Irish boroughs, it enfranchised male householders rated at £4 and upwards. In English counties, tenants paying rates of an annual value of £12 or more and in Scottish counties, £14 tenants and £5 owners were also given the vote. The Irish county franchise was left unchanged. The effect was to give the vote to town artisans, shopkeepers and in England and Scotland, smaller farmers. It added a further million to the voting register making a total of two and a half million (out of a population of 21.4 million, only 1 in 8.5 of the population or 2 in 17 could vote). The minimum size of population needed for a two-membered constituency was raised from 7,000 to 10,000. The seats thus released were redistributed: 25 to new country seats, 9 to new boroughs, 1 to London University and several were added to large towns such as Manchester, Birmingham and Liverpool. England lost 8 seats, Scotland gained 7 and Wales gained 1.

THE BALLOT ACT OF 1872 This made voting at elections secret.

THE FRANCHISE ACT OF 1884 This widened the franchise still further and in particular enfranchised agricultural labourers. The Act made the borough householder's franchise £10 annual value throughout the UK, extended the lodger franchise of 1867 to Ireland and made the county franchise also a £10 annual value throughout the UK. The electorate was now nearly 5 million (1 in 5.4 of the population could vote).

REDISTRIBUTION OF SEATS ACT OF 1885 This abolished 160 seats by disenfranchising all boroughs of less than 15,000 people, merging them into county constituencies and limiting the counties of Hereford and

PARLIAMENTARY REFORM

[illegible]

Rutland and all towns of less than 50,000 population to one member each. The City of London and towns with a population between 50,000 and 165,000 were to have two members. All other areas were to have single member constituencies. The result gave London 37 more members, Lancashire 15 more, England as a whole 6 more and Scotland 12 more.

1911 A bill for universal male suffrage.

1918 Limited votes for women depending on age, financial status and marital status. The vote was granted to all women over 30 who were ratepayers or married to ratepayers.

1928 The beginning of universal franchise. All men and women over 21 were allowed to vote.

Tell the children about the class structure of society in Victorian Britain. Explain the numerical and economic importance of the working classes. Briefly mention the working class movements including Chartism, the Co-operative movement, trade unions and the rise of the Labour Party. Show how these movements have contributed to society in the 20th. century. Pick out individuals for pupils to consider more closely. Let them write thumb-nail sketches of the most important/interesting of these. Pupils can contribute to time-lines of the most important events. e.g.

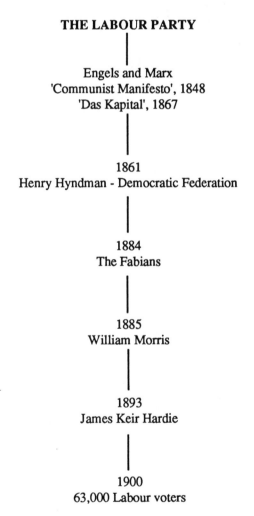

THE LABOUR PARTY

|

Engels and Marx
'Communist Manifesto', 1848
'Das Kapital', 1867

|

1861
Henry Hyndman - Democratic Federation

|

1884
The Fabians

|

1885
William Morris

|

1893
James Keir Hardie

|

1900
63,000 Labour voters

If illustrations and drawings are added these become valuable displays.
In this work especially follow the interest of the children and recount events as 'stories' and the 'lives' of the most important historical players.

There are many cartoons lampooning the main protagonists in these political or pseudo political areas. Find out if the children can understand some of them. The magazine *Punch* is useful here. See booklist.

THE CRIMEAN WAR

It is important at the outset to explain where the Crimea was. The causes and results of the war are important and they are summarised below. Remember that the war was mismanaged by the British. Soldiers were badly equipped and contracted cholera, malaria and dysentery. Tell the story of the Charge of the Light Brigade, a disaster in military history in the 19th. century. Out of 673 men who made the charge only 50 survived unhurt. 113 were killed and most of the others were captured and wounded - all the result of confused orders. Read the classic poem by Lord Tennyson on this subject to the children.

Finally, remember the work of the Angel of Mercy at Scutari. With her 38 nurses, Florence Nightingale helped thousands of wounded soldiers. Her work also made the nursing profession more respectable and more respected. Also mention the contribution of Mary Seacole.

CAUSES

1. Russia wanted to expand at the expense of Turkish territory and in particular to acquire Constantinople and gain free access to the Mediterranean for her commerce and fleet.
2. The British feared Russian expansion regarding it as a danger to Europe, likely to change the balance of power in the Mediterranean and posing a threat to India.
3. Napoleon III wanted to strengthen his precarious throne by the glory and success of an external war.
4. Napoleon also wanted to avenge the personal indignity he felt because Czar Nicholas had refused to recognise his claim to royal rank.
5. In 1852 the ancient squabble between the Orthodox (Greek) and the Roman Catholic Churches about the custody of the Holy Places in Jerusalem surfaced: *The quarrel between two packs of monks about a key and silver star was a trivial symbol of the vast rivalry of centuries between poweful churches, between great states, betweem heterogenous races.* Napoleon intervened successfully with the Turks on behalf of the Catholic claims. Czar Nicholas, as head of the Greek Church, resented this and demanded from Turkey the express recognition of his right to protect all Turkish subjects who belonged to the Greek Church. This would have enabled Russia to interfere constantly in Turkish affairs. The Sultan, with British encouragement, refused, whereupon Russian troops invaded the Turkish Danubian provinces of Moldavia and Wallachia planning to occupy them until the Sultan gave way. Britain and France sent an ultimatum to the Czar demanding the withdrawal of his troops from Turkish territory. No reply was received and the Allies declared war on Russia in March, 1854.

RESULTS

1. The Treaty of Paris (March 1856) provided that the Black Sea was to be neutralised and closed to all warships. Russian secured the cancellation of this proviso in 1871.
2. Sebastopol was not to be fortified again. Russia did not observe this.
3. The Danube was to be open for navigation to ships of all nations. Its waterway was placed under the control of an International Commission consisting of one representative of Turkey and one of each of the great European Powers.
4. The Sultan undertook to grant religious liberty to all his Christian subjects. This undertaking proved worthless.
5. The powers agreed not to use the privileges of the Sultan's Christian subjects as a pretext for interference in Turkey's internal affairs.
6. Britain, France and Austria pledged themseles to maintain the integrity of the Turkey Empire.
7. After further negotiations the Principalities of Moldavia and Wallachia were formally united in 1861 into an autonomous state (Rumania) paying an annual tribute to and acknowledging the suzerainty of the Sultan.
8. The withdrawal of British troops from India to the Crimea and exaggerated reports of British military disasters in the war were contributory causes of the Indian Mutiny.
9. National ill-feeling between Britain and Russia intensified and Russia began seriously to plan advances into central Asia.
10. In Britain, the Aberdeen ministry fell, Gladstone's seven-year plan for reconstructing the national finances was set back, Palmerston became the national idol and retained his supreme position until his death in 1865. The war, Gladstone said afterwards, gave to Turkey, for the first time perhaps in her bloodstained history, twenty years of repose not disturbed either by herself or by a foreign power.

Pinpoint the places and the battles: Alma - a pyrrhic victory; Balaclava - Russians driven off; Inkerman - another Russian failure and Sebastopol - allies bombarded the town for nearly a year.

TROUBLE IN THE COLONIES

THE INDIAN MUTINY

CAUSES

1. The East India Company was primarily a commercial organisation trading for profit and its exploitation of India's resources and frequent oppressive actions were responsible for widespread and deep-seated discontent.
2. Lord Dalhousie's annexations and interference in the administration of the native states had greatly alarmed and angered the Indian princes.
3. Dalhousie's reforms in the adjustment of land settlements had created much uneasiness and discontent among the landowning classes.
4. Religions fanaticism and superstition: the Brahmins and other high-caste Hindus bitterly resented Dalhousie's efforts to suppress such 'religious' barbarities as suttee and infanticide.
5. The tactless aggressiveness of British missionaries angered the Moslems and the higher caste Hindus and alarmed the masses, who were told by their native superiors that the English intended to force them to become Christians.
6. A scheme of the British authorities to make all native entrants into the Bengal army liable for service overseas greatly disturbed the native troops, for if they crossed the sea they would lose their caste.
7. The native soldiers had to bite off the end of a new, improved type of cartridge before loading it into their guns. Indian priests spread a report that the new cartridges were greased with a mixture of cow-fat and hog's lard. The cow was sacred to the Hindus and the pig unclean to Moslems and so both Hindus and Moslems who bit the cartridges would be polluted: the Hindus would lose caste and Moslems their hope of Paradise. The actual start of the Mutiny was the refusal of native soldiers (called Sepoys) to touch these cartridges. They were imprisoned for disobedience, released by their comrades who shot their officers and started to march to Delhi to proclaim a native emperor.
8. There was a prophecy that British rule would come to an end exactly a hundred years after the Battle of Plassey (1757) and there was a widespread Moslem conspiracy to revive the Mogul empire.
9. The British army in India was weak because regiments had been drafted to the Crimea and a force had been sent to China.
10. Exaggerated stories had been circulated of British disasters in the Crimean War.

EXTENT

The Mutiny spread through northern India and down the Ganges valley to Patna, but Calcutta was quiet, most of the Punjab was loyal and there were only small local outbreaks in the territories of Bombay and Madras.

RESULTS

1. The East India Company was abolished.
2. The India Act of 1858 placed India and its dependencies under the control of the British Crown, to be administered by a Secretary of State, aided by a Council of India consisting of civil and military officers, lawyers and merchants with long experience of Indian affairs. The Governor-General of India was to be the representative of the Secretary of State.
3. The Act provided for the complete re-organisation of the Indian Army. A major proviso was that no Indian troops should be employed outside India without the express approval of the British Parliament.

THE ZULU WAR

The threat of the Zulus to British settlers in South Africa meant that British troops were sent out to protect them. In January 1879 a British contingent invaded Zululand to' teach the natives a lesson'. Part of this force of 1,500 men were attacked by over 20,000 Zulu warriors at Isandhlwana. All the British soldiers perished in the massacre. Shortly after this engagement a handful of British soldiers, certainly not more than 200 in all, defended themselves against 4,000 Zulus who attacked them at the mission hospital of Rorke's Drift. The soldiers, vastly outnumbered, fought bravely to the last man and eleven Victoria Crosses were awarded after the battle. By July, 1879 the British using superior weapons including Gatling guns had defeated the Zulus, destroyed their capital of Ulundi and captured Cetewayo, their king. The Zulu war was over.

Such stories are useful vehicles for teaching history. Explain the extent of the British Empire in Victoria's day and that such a large territory was bound to have problems. These episodes show problems on two contrasting continents - India and Africa. Again, let the children investigate the leaders in these episodes and let them read extracts from *The Times* and the *Illustrated London News* about events as they occurred. If the language is too difficult read the extracts or paraphrase them in simple English. Make sure that the children understand the vocabulary and explain words like Sepoys and Zulus. Let the children describe the battle scenes and if possible, draw them.

THE SUEZ CANAL
VICTORIA, EMPRESS OF INDIA

SUEZ

In 1869, the Suez Canal was opened to traffic. This international waterway had been designed and built by the famous French engineer, Ferdinand de Lesseps. The canal changed the sea-route from England to India, and transferred to Egypt much of the strategic importance which formerly belonged to the Cape of Good Hope.

Britain had no interest in this new vital artery but the Khedive of Egypt, Ismael, had shares in the Suez Canal Company which he wished to sell. He agreed to sell them to Britain for £4 million and he also suggested that Britain should buy up the whole of the shares in the Company. The Foreign Office rejected the overtures probably because in these early years Suez was unprofitable. By November 1875 the Khedive's financial position worsened and he started negotiations to sell the shares to two French groups. Disraeli heard that the shares were again on the market and with the aid of the bankers Rothschilds bought them for Britain. The decision, which was entirely Disraeli's, showed him to be very shrewd: during the fifty years following the purchase the £4 million was repaid in dividends and interest paid over eight times (a profit of 800%!).

EMPRESS OF INDIA

Another brain-child of Disraeli's was the addition of the words 'Empress of India' to Queen Victoria's titles. The Prime Minister considered that it would give the Queen much prestige on the Indian sub-continent and despite opposition in the Commons and the Lords, the new title became law (1876). The Queen was very annoyed by the opposition's attitude but was so pleased with Disraeli she made him an earl. The magazine *Punch* depicted the event.

New Crowns for Old

Use a globe with the children or an atlas to show the location of the Suez Canal. From the map it will be clear to them that distances to India and the Far East were cut by the canal. Explain that the Canal took ten years to build and was financed with French and Turkish money. Pinpoint the Canal on the map - over 100 miles long, it takes ships fifteen hours to travel through it. Explain the distances involved. It reduced the journey from Britain to India by 4,000 miles. Encourage the children to sketch a map of Africa showing the effect of the Suez canal on travel. Discuss other 'arteries' that have helped communication such as Kiel, Panama. If possible turn this into a general discussion about how the world has 'shrunk' because of advances in technology such as telephones, telegraphs, computers, fax machines, aeroplanes, the Channel Tunnel and satellites.

Canals might lead into a discussion of British canals and their importance before railways. Explain why canals are not so important today as they were.

Discuss the importance of India in Victoria's Empire and the attitudes to her adopting the title. Using the cartoon from *Punch*, ask the children 'obvious' but pertinent questions. [E.g. Who are the characters? What is being offered by each? What is the significance of 'new crowns for old' - can they see the Aladdin connection, i.e. the way Disraeli is dressed - genie of the lamp?]

A VICTORIAN SUCCESS STORY
THE GREAT EXHIBITION, 1851

On 1 May, 1851 Queen Victoria opened the Great Exhibition in the Crystal Palace, Hyde Park, London. The Exhibition building was designed by Joseph Paxton and made entirely of iron and glass. The iron framework was lifted into place a section at a time by two huge cranes. Prince Albert's opening speech published in the official catalogue of the Great Exhibition gives some interesting details.

The number of Exhibitors whose productions it has been found possible to accommodate is about 15,000 of whom nearly one-half are British. The remainder represent the productions of more than forty foreign countries, comprising almost the whole of the civilized nations of the globe. In arranging the space to be allotted to each, we have taken into consideration both the nature of its productions and the facility of access to this country afforded by its geographical position. Your Majesty will find the productions of Your Majesty's dominions arranged in the western portion of the Building, and those of foreign countries in the eastern. The Exhibition is divided into the four great classes of 1. Raw materials; 2. Machinery; 3. Manufactures; and 4. Sculpture and the Fine Arts. A further division has been made according to the geographical position of the countries represented; those which lie within the warmer latitudes being placed near the centre of the Building, and the colder countries at the extremities.

The work was completed in record time.

Your Majesty having been graciously pleased to grant a site in this your Royal park for the purposes of the Exhibition, the first column of the structure now honoured by Your Majesty's presence was fixed on the 26th. of September last. Within the short period, therefore, of seven months, owing to the energy of the Contractors, and the active industry of the workmen employed by them a building has been erected, Entirely novel in its construction, covering a space of more than 18 acres, measuring 1,851 feet in length, and 456 in extreme breadth, capable of containing 40,000 visitors, and affording a frontage for the Exhibition of Goods to the extent of more than 10 miles. For the original suggestion of the principle of this structure, the Commissioners are indebted to Mr Joseph Paxton, to whom they feel their acknowledgements to be justly due for this interesting feature of their undertaking.

Huge crowds flocked to see the wonders being shown including a steam hammer, steam locomotives, an envelope-making machine and a cast-iron fountain. There was also a model of the Liverpool Docks with 1,600 fully rigged ships.

On 2 May, 1851 *The Times* reported:

There was yesterday witnessed a sight the like of which has never happened before, and which, in the nature of things, can never be repeated ... In a building that could easily have accommodated twice as many, twenty-five thousand persons, so it is computed, were arranged in order round the throne of our Sovereign. Around them, amidst them, and over their heads was displayed all that is useful or beautiful in nature or in art. Above them rose a glittering arch far more lofty and spacious than the vaults of even our noblest cathedrals. On either side the vista seemed almost boundless ... Some saw in it the second and more glorious inaugauration of their Sovereign; some a solemn dedication of art and its stores; some were most reminded of that day when all ages and climes shall be gathered round the throne of the Maker; there was so much that seemed accidental and yet had a meaning, that no one could be content with simply what he saw ... all contributed to an effect so grand and yet so natural, that it hardly seemed to be put together by design, or to be the work of human artificers.

The Exhibition was the brain-child of Prince Albert. It was very successful with over 100,000 different exhibits including those loaned by the Queen herself, for example the Koh-i-Noor diamond. Models of all types, agricultural tools, household equipment, clocks, furniture, pottery of all kinds, scientific instruments, a model locomotive, a fire engine from Canada and a display of Samuel Colt's revolvers from America were on show.

Admission to the public cost one shilling from Mondays to Thursdays and half-a-crown and a crown on Fridays and Saturdays (2/6d and 5s). The Exhibition lasted for five months and over 6 million people visited it, many coming by trains organised by the first travel agent, Thomas Cook.

There was no doubt that the Exhibition was an outstanding success. Built by 2,260 men in less than 7 months, it showed British achievements in all their glory and emphasised that this country was the 'workshop

A VICTORIAN SUCCESS STORY
THE GREAT EXHIBITION 1851

of the world'.

After the Exhibition, the Crystal Palace building was dismantled and rebuilt in South London. Unfortunately, it was destroyed by fire in November, 1936.

The Great Exhibition is an excellent vehicle for work by the class. Tell them all about the Exhibition and how Prince Albert thought it up. Show them pictures and drawings of it being built explaining the problems that the workmen had from nesting sparrows (until the Duke of Wellington suggested using sparrowhawks to frighten them away).

Emphasise the problems of organising such a huge event, especially without the aid of modern technology and communications. Let the children organise an 'exhibition' of their own so that they can experience the kinds of problems involved. Older children might attempt a model or diorama of the building. They could fill their model with typical exhibits. Allow the children to research the objects and machines available in 1851 and decide which would be of particular interest to visitors and why.

Discuss the logistics of so many people visiting the capital to see the exhibition in an age when there were no cars and no tubes.

Let them write an imaginary account of a visit to the 'Great Exhibition'. They can imagine they are on their own, with their family or on a school visit. Let them record what they wear, their travel arrangements, what they eat en route ... Description is essential, especially their initial reactions to the huge exhibition building and what they thought about the exhibits. They may prefer to write the account as a diary.

Some of the children may have been to modern shows or exhibitons such as the Boat Show , the Ideal Home Exhibition or the Motor Show. Ask them to compare and contrast this with the Great Exhibition. What would not have been available in 1851 which would be available today? (Electricity, telephone, fax, TV, sophisticated advertising devices ...)

PHOTOGRAPHY

Photography became possible as a result of two inventions which were made public in 1839: daguerreotypy and calotypy. Louis Daguerre of Paris produced an image on light sensitive silver iodide, developed it in mercury vapour and fixed it with common salt. This method produced a single, uncopyable print. The English squire, Fox Talbot's calotype process produced a negative on light-sensitive paper which could be used to make any number of copies. Subjects had to remain still for a long time, 15 minutes or more, but these first steps in photography were very important. It could be used for factual and accurate recording, for illustration, for pictorial representation, for the expression of ideas in realistic or abstract form. In 1851, the wet-collodion process made 'instant' exposures possible. (Subjects still had to sit without moving for long periods of time by today's standards.) The light sensitive surface was deposited on glass plates which had to be developed immediately. This meant that the photographer had to take a portable dark room with him if he wanted to take photographs outside his studio. Nevertheless, it enabled cameramen to take the first 'news' photographs. Roger Fenton visited the Crimea and successfully captured the atmosphere of war.

Sitting perfectly still for 15 minutes in bright sunlight was not enjoyed by all subjects! They were not always pleased with the results either. Red faces came out black until they learned to powder them with flour. Painters could flatter their sitters but the camera showed up people's wrinkles, frown lines and crooked noses. At first only the beautiful would be photographed but as techniques improved Victorians were keen to have a family portrait taken. They still had to pose for quite long periods of time and this explains why the photographs tend to look stiff. Lewis Carroll was a keen photographer and Queen Victoria also tried her hand with a camera.

Discuss the importance of the early steps in photography. Encourage the children to bring 'old' and new photographs to class and compare them. Ask the children to sit perfectly still. How long can they manage this? Old Victorian postcards, many of which have been re-issued, and cigarette cards are interesting. Encourage the children to make moving pictures and their own flip books. (See end of Teachers' Notes.)

Discuss why photographs usually look more natural today and the social influence of the snapshot. Photography has become an accurate, instant way of recording history in the making. It is an invaluable scientific technique. Now photography records objects too small, too distant, and too fast or slow moving to be seen by the human eye.

EXPLORERS AND MISSIONARIES

Exploring has always been fashionable. Over 4,000 years ago the King of Egypt sent Harkhuf further into Africa to seek rare woods and treasure. Many Victorians were eager to explore territories in different parts of the world. Their reasons were diverse: to trade, to solve a geographical problem, to find new territory for the British Empire, to convert people to the Christian faith ...

In the 18th. century wealthy citizens had formed the African Society which aimed to explore Africa and a young Scottish doctor, Mungo Park, undertook several expeditions into the continent. Sadly, after November, 1805 nothing more was heard of him and his quest to find the mouth of the River Niger.

More expeditions were undertaken in the 19th. century. Some of the most important were

1829 - 33 James Clark Ross became the first man to discover the North Magnet Pole and the ice shelf named after him, Ross Ice Shelf.
1848 - Alfred Wallace and Henry Bates explored the Amazon in South America and reached Manaus.
1853 - Richard Burton (in disguise) became the first white person to enter the holy Muslim city of Mecca.
1856 - David Livingstone, the most famous African explorer, crossed Africa.
1857 - John Hanning Speake explored the great lakes of equatorial Africa. By 1860 he had found and named Lake Victoria and guessed that this lake was the source of the Nile.
1862 - William Palgrave crossed Arabia.
1866 - Samuel and Florence Baker reached Lake Albert in Africa.
1865 - Edward Whymper climbed the highest mountains in the Andes.
1871 - Henry Stanley, sent out by the America newspaper, the *New York Herald,* to find Livingstone met him at Ujiji in East Africa.
1877 - Stanley travelled down the River Congo.
1891 - Younghusband crossed the Gobi Desert.

Explorations fire young minds and children enjoy hearing stories about great expeditions and the characters who undertook them. Such expeditions were written about in the 19th. century and copies of *The Times* and the *Illustrated London News* have accounts of some of these journeys. Let the children choose one of the explorers and one of their expeditions to research.

Point out the bravery of such individuals remembering that Africa in the 19th. century was known as *the white man's grave*. Work out a time-line of expeditions and discoveries or a chart to show what was undiscovered in 1800 and what had been found by 1901 when Victoria died. Make inventories of what explorers had to take with them and pinpoint the perils they faced - unfamiliar climates, disease, dangerous wild animals such as snakes and disease carrying insects, unfriendly natives, superstition, difficult terrain to navigate to name but a few.

[Remember to point out that the names of such discoveries as Lake Victoria and Lake Albert were given to them when they were found by British explorers.]

THE IRISH PROBLEM

It seems that there has always been an Irish problem. In reality, there were many problems. These include

1. The Irish had been subjects of the English crown since the 12th. century and they had been neglected by Britain all this time.
2. The Irish rebelled against English rule. Because of this, the lands of the rebel Irish were given (a) to English and Scottish settlers, (b) to English and Scottish nobles.
3. Also these English and Scottish people were mainly protestants. The Irish were mainly catholics.
4. Many of the English and Scottish landowners did not live in Ireland: they were absentee landlords and were represented by agents.
5. These agents rack-rented the tenants, that is they made them pay a high rent which nearly equalled the value of the property rented.
6. Three-quarters of the Irish did not own the land on which they lived.
7. Parliamentary reform and catholic emancipation promised by England was slow in coming.
8. The situation was further exacerbated by the failure of food crops and general famine.

As far as Britain was concerned, Ireland was first a source of raw materials for the English textile industry and a large source of provisions. It became an exporter of woollen and then of linen manufactures and in the 18th. century was a great exporting granary. Then by a series of repressive laws, the trade of Ireland was crippled and the Irish Catholics depressd and degraded. Yet the population grew. Potatoes were the mainstay of the Irish diet and these thrived in the moist, rich Irish soil. As the population grew and the demand for land and potatoes rose, landowners raised their rents exacting as much as they could from the people. Tenure of land was precarious, usually from one year to the next. All improvements to the land were carried out by the peasants. The cottier built his hut, fenced his land and drained it, all at his own expense. The situation worsened and there was deep dissatisfaction and resentment. Then there was famine and rebellion.

In 1800 the population of Ireland was about 5·25 millions. The Period of the Napoleonic Wars brought great but artificial prosperity to Ireland, as it did to English farmers and manufacturers and the Irish population increased to over 8 millons by 1841. But Irish manufacturing was now declining. It could not compete against the machine production of the British factory system. Ireland did not have the same advantage as England with regard to coal. The seams of the Irish coal fields were thin, the quality of the coal poor and industry was not close to the coalfields. The extraction and transport of Irish coal was expensive.

Then came the great Famine. The disease called blight destroyed the potato crop in 1845 and returned to decimate the crop again in the following year (1846). An enormous tragedy ensued. Through emigration and death from starvation or from disease, the population dropped by more than 2 millions between 1845 and 1855. From this time, agriculture and population showed a steady decline. The acreage of corn crops in 1847 was 3·3 millions, in 1869 it was 2·6 and in 1900 it was only 1·5 millions. The population of 5·75 millions in 1860 was less than 4·5 millions in 1900.

Punch interpreted the impossibilities of dealing with the land problem in this cartoon showing Gladstone grappling with a bull.

THE IRISH PROBLEM

Tillage dropped mainly because of competition from the cheap corn from the virgin lands of America. Between 1870 and 1900, the Land Acts operated to break up the old large estates. Under the Acts nearly 300,000 holdings were set up but most of them were under 30 acres and many were unecomomic. Wide areas of rich grassland would have been better used as grazing for stock than split up into small holdings. But political ignorance and sentimentalism and the mania of the peasant for his plot, whether it be of value or not, overbore economic sense in the settlements.

The British government was slow to help the peasants. The Irish land problem was intractable and many peasant farmers were evicted by landowners (many of these landowners still lived in England or Scotland).

RESULTS AND EFFECTS

1. With the agricultural and general trade depression after Waterloo, Irish emigration to England increased. By 1837 there were over 100,000 Irish in Lancashire alone. Between 1847 and 1851 over half a million came, mainly to the North, but also to South Wales.
2. The emigrants were seen as a great burden on towns where filth and poverty were already unmanageable problems.
3. The emigrants caused problems in industry: they accepted lower wages than the English and were exploited by employers to keep wages down and to break strikes, they were considered to be insubordinate workers and quarrelsome.
4. They also caused serious religious riots.
5. The agrarian disorders with their shootings, arson, cattle-maiming and murders made Coercion Acts a part of nearly every parliament. 26 such Acts were passed between 1800 and 1866.
6. The stream of Irish emigrating to the USA took with them their economic and political grievances against the English, embittering relations between America and England. Much of the violence and separatist propaganda of the latter part of the century was planned and financed by the Irish in America.
7. Between 1875 - 1886, the progress of English domestic legislation was greatly disrupted by Irish obstruction in the Commons. This caused the introduction of the closure which has permanently weakened the effective supervision of the financial Estimates by the Commons.
8. It was the economic grievances that supplied the driving force of the Home Rule movement.

In 1859 a secret society called the Fenian Brotherhood was inaugurated. Its aim was to make Ireland independent, by force if necessary. They tried to take Chester Castle and blew up a London prison killing 12. In 1870 an Irish Home Rule Party was formed, soon joined by 50 MPs. Charles Stuart Parnell became leader but the violence continued. In 1882, Irish terroists murdered Lord Cavendish and his under-secretary in Pheonix Park, Dublin.

Gladstone, the Prime Minister, eventually supported Home Rule and attempted to get it through by Act of Parliament. Twice, a bill to bring about this was thrown out by the House of Lords and Parnell lost his leadership of the Irish through a scandal.

The children should know about the plight of Ireland and how the Irish problem was mismanaged in this period. Duscuss the position of the peasants and the landowners. Explain why the Irish emigrants were useful in Britain and elsewhere. Compare and contrast the Irish problems in the 19th. and 20th. centuries. Get the children to draw cartoons to illustrate any Irish problems.

Illustrate how Ireland has been a problem since the 12th. century and mention the Irish problem today - the IRA and the Loyalists. Describe how the present crisis might be settled - the cessation of violence by both factions and surrender of all weapons and arms.

THE EASTERN QUESTION

The Eastern Question was the problem of the survival or dismemberment of the old Ottoman Empire. In the 19th. century Turkey, the centre of this ancient Empire was regarded as the *sick man of Europe*. The problem first arose when Peter the Great, realising that Russia (to become a great commercial nation) needed access to the Black Sea, attacked Turkey. In the 18th. century Russia and Austria (the latter wanted control of the Danube) persistently attacked the Turks. France was the first power to appreciate the menace of Russia's advance towards the Mediterranean and supported Turkey. Towards the end of the century, England awoke to the danger and Pitt would have also supported them, but public opinion was too strong for him because of the great ill-feeling there was against France at the time. Then came Bonaparte who invaded Egypt and Syria intending to conquer the Balkans and India but in 1802 by the Treaty of Amiens, France recognised Egypt as the possession of Turkey. The Eastern Questions influenced British foreign policy throughout the 19th. century.

1. It made English statesmen very suspicious of Russia and all except Gladstone were sympathetic towards Turkey.
2. It involved England in the Crimean War.
3. It twice created serious friction between England and France.
4. It brought about the downfall of Disraeli and raised Gladstone to the height of his power.
5. The English policy of preserving Turkey deflected the course of Russian expansion in Central Asia with consequent menace to India. England was involved in two Afghan wars and nearly in a war with Russia itself.

FACTORS IN THE EASTERN QUESTION

1. In 1821 the Greeks revolted against the oppressive government of the Turks.
2. In 1827 under the Treaty of London, France, Russia and England agreed jointly to persuade or compel the Sultan of Turkey to grant self-government under his suzerainty to Greece.
3. Through a misunderstanding, a battle (Navarino) occurred between the allied fleet and the Egyptian and Turkish fleets in which the Turkish fleet was totally destroyed. The English government refused to take any further action but Turkey acknowledged the independence of Greece in 1829.
4. In 1839 Mehemet Ali, the Pasha of Egypt, revolted against the Sultan and invaded Syria. The hostilities at sea interfered with England's Black Sea trade but apart from this Palmerston was determined to maintain the Sultan's domains intact. The British fleet bombarded Acre and forced Mehemet to evacuate Syria. France favoured the Pasha and the contest nearly brought war with England.
5. The Crimean War.
6. In 1875 - 6 the Turks suppressed with great severity revolts of their non-Muslim subjects in Herzegovina and Bulgaria. Further risings followed in Bosnia, Servia and Montenegro, which were also crushed. Then in 1877 Russia, claiming to be the protector of the Slavs, invaded the Balkans, defeated the Turks after fierce fighting at Plevna, entered Adrianople and reached the Sea of Marmora, where at San Stefano in March 1878 she imposed a treaty on Turkey. This deprived Turkey of Kars, Batum, Bessarabia and most of its Balkan territory.
7. Meanwhile Disraeli mobilised the army reserve and sent Indian troops to Malta and the British fleet to the Dardanelles. Russia was warned that if her troops went into Constantinople, it would mean war with England. Disraeli also demanded that the Treaty of San Stefano should be submitted to a congress of the European Powers for revision. Russia conceded. The Powers met and by the Treaty of Berlin, July 1878, Russia retained Kars, Batum and Bessarabia. Bosnia and Hertzegovina were assigned to Austria-Hungary. Rumania, Servia and Montenegro were made independent principalities. Two self-governing provinces under the suzerainty of Turkey were set up and named Bulgaria and Eastern Romania.
   A month earlier Disraeli had made an agreement with the Sultan that, in return for the cession of Cyprus, England would pay him an annual tribute and guarantee to defend Turkey against any Russian aggression in Asia.
8. In1881 there was a great nationalist insurrection in Egypt. This caused great friction between England and France. England wanted the Sultan of Turkey to restore order. France and Russia did not agree and England had to cope with the situation alone.
   The problem of Turkey continued throughout Victoria's reign and it was no accident that the beginnings of the Great War (1914-18) stemmed from the Balkans.

Again, to give an account of the Eastern Question it is necessary to start with an atlas. Let the children pinpoint Turkey on the map. Show how this country felt surrounded. Outline how the Eastern Question led to a number of wars in the 19th. century. Examine what effects the problems in the Balkans had on British policies and on social life here. Briefly discuss the present problems in the area resulting from the end of the Cold War, the changes in Russian politics and the collapse of Yugoslavia.

CULTURE AND VICTORIAN BRITAIN

ART AND LITERATURE

The Victorian period was a time of sharp contrasts: between immense wealth and squalid poverty, between powered vehicles and horse-drawn transport, between machines and manual labour, between indifference to culture and concern/obsession with it.

ART AND ARTEFACTS

Culturally, Victorians were concerned with improving artistic standards. John Ruskin dictated taste in architecture and painting. Pagin, Prince Albert, Henry Cole, Charles Locke Eastlake and Owen Jones were also influential through public and literary works. In 1849 Henry Cole began to commission artists to design articles in glass, ceramics and silver. He then launched Felix Summerby's Art Manufactures as a commercial venture. He also wrote children's books and designed glass himself. Later, he was to be the chief reformer of the national design schools and the founder of what is now the Victoria and Albert Museum.

Numerous exhibitions added to these cultural movements. By 1843 Prince Albert had become President of the Royal Society of Arts and with Henry Cole started a series of exhibitions of British Art Manufacturers. In 1851 the Great Exhibition was a huge success. This was followed in 1857 by the Manchester Art Treasures Exhibition. Industrial exhibitions both national and international continued until the end of the century.

HAND-CRAFTSMANSHIP

The teachings of Ruskin and the Gothic revivalists led to the importance of hand-craftsmanship. The leading exponent of this was William Morris. At this time (1862) the influence of the the art and artefacts of Japan had great artistic and cultural significance. *Japanism* was seen in the design of all kinds of commercial and hand-crafted objects. The aesthetic movement had begun.

THE PRE-RAPHAELITES

In 1848 a group of young British artists including Dante Gabriel Rossetti, John Everett Millais and William Holman Hunt found themselves in sympathy with Italian art of the 15th. century. This group became known as the Pre-Raphaelites. The influence of Japan also flourished in art and the famous American artist, James Abbot McNeill Whistler, brought the Impressionist influence of Monet and Degas to this country.

LITERATURE

The Victorian period was a time when novels became popular and were read by the upper and middle classes. Many of them started life by being serialised in magazines and newspapers. Books like *Jane Eyre* and *Wuthering Heights* by the Bronté sisters (Anne, Emily and Charlotte) were popular. Thomas Hardy had also begun writing and *Far from the Madding Crowd* was serialised in 1873. Publication of *Tess of the d'Urbervilles* in 1891 caused a furore in Victorian polite society. The most famous Victorian writer was Charles Dickens (1812 - 1870). His books about Victorian life are social documentaries on the period. Designed principally for adults, they tell us much about the lives of children in the 19th. century. He drew attention to the social conditions which brought poverty, disease and humiliation to most of the people. His books have social and moral messages and contain an abundance of historical material.

Books for children were few and far between. Many children (as well as adults) could not read and relied on others to read to them. In 1863 Charles Kingsley wrote his classic book for children, *The Water Babies*. The first book designed to entertain children was Lewis Carroll's *Alice's Adventures in Wonderland*. This was followed by adventure stories such as Robert Louis Stevenson's *Treasure Island*, Captain Marryat's *The Children of the New Forest* and Charles Kingsley's *Westward Ho*. There were also stories about animals like Anna Sewell's *Black Beauty*. Victorian children also read fairy stories by the Brothers Grimm and Hans Christian Andersen. Magazines or *weeklies* became popular after the 1850s. There were *The Boys Own Paper* (price 1d), Little *Folks* or *Chums* and books with games and hobbies like *The Girls Own* book. Many children bought comics called *penny dreadfuls* such as *The Skeleton Band* or *Boy Burglar* which sometimes contained violent and frightening material.

Discuss the art, architecture and artefacts of Victorian times with the children. More important, take them to places where they can see examples of Victorian work. Note the ornateness and decorative work of the time. Point out such embellishments not only on artefacts but on buildings in cities. Consider the cost of such work today. Contrast Victorian architecture and present-day work. Let them see the work of the famous designer William Morris. Compare manufactured products such as cards, postcards, serviettes and fans from Victorian times with items. Discuss the materials available then and compare with what is available now.

Read suitable excerpts from Dickens, the Brontës, Hardy and others. Dickens is especially valuable as you can choose parts of his novels which have social history messages. Let the children look for clues in adult novels and children's books which tell them the books were written in Victorian times. Dickens is easily adapted to drama and children enjoy playing the parts. Oliver asking for more is always a favourite. Children's books written in Victorian times should also be read to the children. Discuss why the works are typically nineteenth century.

VICTORIAN PASTIMES AND ENTERTAINMENT

By 1850 many people were earning more money and hours of work were shorter as the Factory Acts were passed. People began to have leisure time to enjoy sports and other activities. Workers' *days out* to the seaside became popular and the development of the railways from the 1860s made them possible: many trains went to the fashionable resorts. In 1871 Parliament passed a law giving workers six paid bank holidays annually.

Theatres became very popular and most offered variety entertainment. Many of the shows were of the music hall type, audience participation was important and made it all the more fun. Enthusiastic audiences watched as many as 40 acts or turns in an evening including singers, dancers, comedians, conjurers, magicians and musicians. Terry's Theatre in London was a typical example but there were at least 30 in the East End. Famous music hall entertainers included Marie Lloyd, Little Tich, Stan Laurel and Charlie Chaplin. Circuses and fairs also provided entertainment.

New parks, museums and places of recreation were beginning to emerge and trains made it possible for people to go away to resorts such as Brighton, Ramsgate and Scarborough. In these resorts huge family hotels and boarding houses sprang up to accommodate the visitors. Sea bathing and boating and, in the 1870s, roller skating became popular. Croquet and lawn tennis also became fashionable.

As roads improved, people took to cycling. The early bicycle, with a big front wheel and a small back wheel (the penny-farthing) was difficult and uncomfortable to ride. When the safety bicycle appeared in 1885 (this had both wheels the same size) more people took to the road: townspeople rode into the countryside for pleasure and picnics.

The rich and upper middle classes enjoyed visits to the theatre, opera, pantomimes and racing. Many learned to dance and attended lavish balls. Some made their own entertainments: singing, playing the piano and playing charades at home. The poor in towns were entertained on the street. Singers, acrobats, barrel-organs, clowns, performing animals and Punch and Judy shows were popular.

Indoors, children played cards, dominoes, draughts and chess. They collected pressed flowers, stamps, cards, photographs, coins and pictures. Outside they played ball, hoops, marbles, spinning tops and skipping. They liked magic lanterns shows and peepshows - fast moving pictures which they could watch through small apertures.

Games such as football and cricket had been played for centuries but during Victorian times they became better organised and common rules were adopted. In 1855 the first football club, Sheffield Football Club, was formed and adopted a set of rules (Sheffield Club Rules). In 1863 the Football Association was formed and devised a set of rules for all football clubs to follow. During the1880s many of today's football league clubs were established.

English and Australian teams played the first cricket Test Match in England in 1880 and one well-known batsman was W. G. Grace. Tennis became popular and the first Wimbledon tennis tournament was held in Victorian times.

Discuss Victorian pastimes with the children comparing them with those of today. Look at the way people dressed for leisure. Consider a day at the seaside then and now. Which would they enjoy most and why? Explain what the Victorians meant by a bathing machine and how these were pulled to the edge of the sea by horses. Also show how beaches were segregated at this time. Comparisons and contrasts between then and now might include:

In Victorian times - bathing machines, bathing costumes, separate beaches for men and women, horses, charabancs, many cycles, barrel organs, brass bands, parasols, sailing ships.

Now - undressing on the beach, swimsuits and bikinis, no separate beaches, cars, motor bikes, transistors, deck chairs, speed boats and surfing.

They can also compare and contrast Victorian pastimes with our own. Remember there were no cinemas,no fast food cafés, no radio, no television and no bingo. Comparisons of old postcards with today's is an interesting exercise. Explain why postcards were not sent until the 1860s. Let them make their own Victorian and present-day postcards.

Explain why much of the entertainment, especially at home, was man-made. Get them to play charades and other parlour games. If you can, get them to watch old tyme music hall on television and encourage a class music hall of their own with audience participation. Singing Victorian songs will help to create an atmosphere. A visit to a toy museum which specialises in Victorian toys is also worthwhile.

VICTORIAN DOMESTIC LIFE

In early Victorian days most people lived in the country in small, damp, draughty, ill-lit cottages. As industry developed people migrated to the towns where most lived in overcrowded, terraced houses which were jerrybuilt often back to back. These houses had no running water, no inside bathrooms or toilets or proper drains and no gardens. Water came from local streams, wells, rivers or pumps in the street and was carried in buckets to the houses. There was little furniture and houses were lit by candles or oil lamps. In many ways, living conditions in the towns were worse than in the country.

Factory workers had little time for domestic life. They worked long hours for low wages and most people eked out an existence trying to buy basic needs such as food and clothing. Women took in washing and sewing if they could get it and even children as young as 5 or 6 were sent out to work.

As the century progressed, social reforms undertaken by Lord Shaftesbury and others slowly improved working and living conditions. Edwin Chadwick's report on Public Health shocked the nation and eventually 'clean' drinking water was available for all (1870s). The poor were not only helped by legislation but by private charities such as William Booth's Salvation Army (founded in 1878) and Dr Thomas Barnardo's homes for orphans (1870s). By this time, many industrial areas were so overcrowded that houses were built outside the towns. These were the suburbs. As regular horse-drawn bus services developed and electric trams and steam trains became available many people were able to move to these areas and commute to work. Most suburbs had rows of terraced houses and a number of more expensive ones which were detached.

Victorian families were large, the average family had 5 or 6 children. Most workers lived in terraced housing but the upper and middle classes lived in large, comfortable houses. These upper and middle classes were factory owners, doctors, lawyers, bankers and businesmen. They usually employed servants to look after them and the houses.

The father was the unquestioned head of a Victorian household. He was a stern figure who expected to be obeyed within the family circle. His word was law. He went out to work each day while the mother looked after the house, organised the servants and supervised domestic arrangements. Middle class families had a nursery for the children and a nanny who supervised them. They saw their parents at mealtimes or in the evening before going to bed. Sons were trained for the army or the professions. Girls stayed at home, supervised by a governess and were trained in domestic work. They were expected to make a good match and an early marriage.

All households, except the poorest, employed servants to do the domestic work. Well-off families had cooks, butlers, chauffeurs, footmen, gardeners and a whole entourage of maids and kitchen staff. The cook ran the kitchen and prepared the food. The butler received visitors and waited on the family. The footmen did heavy work like carrying and a gardener cared for the grounds and provided fresh vegetables. The chauffeur looked after transportation including the horses (and later the car/s). A lady's maid attended the wife and housemaids and kitchen maids cleaned the rooms and helped in the kitchen.

ORGANISATION OF A VICTORIAN HOME

GROUND FLOOR

PARLOUR or drawing room (For sitting in and music)	DINING ROOM (Family ate here)	LARGE KITCHEN (Food cooked here)	LARDER (Food stored here)	SCULLERY (Washing up done here)

FIRST FLOOR

BEDROOM I (Family)	BEDROOM 2 (Family)	BEDROOM 3 (Family)	NURSERY (Family. Children slept and played here)

SECOND FLOOR

ATTIC ROOM Servant's room	ATTIC ROOM Servant's room	ATTIC ROOM Servant's room

Most of the larger houses eventually had an indoor toilet. The main rooms were filled with furniture, wax flowers, photographs, pictures and ornaments. In the 1870s gas lights replaced oil lamps and candles and by 1881 some had electric lights. There were no separate bathrooms at first and servants carried jugs of hot water from the kitchen to moveable baths placed in front of bedroom fires. Poor houses had a tin or zinc bath which hung outside the house on a hook on the wall. Miners, for example, washed in such a bath placed in front of the fire. For poorer families it was also the practice for the whole family to wash in the same water usually starting with the smallest child and ending with father.

Discuss the domestic life of Victorian familes including family life for the different classes. Show how their lives differed from ours, especially with reference to the attitude to women and children.Comment on the hierarchy of a typical upper or middle class family particularly the upstairs - downstairs relationships. If possible let the children see an episode of the television series, *Upstairs Downstairs.* Examine a Victorian house and show where people lived in this establishment.

Discuss the position of women in relation to not only homelife but to their legal rights - including property and voting rights. Let the chidlren pretend to be the children of a Victorian family and write about their lives. Role play can be useful here with some taking the roles of master, mistress and children and others being servants.

SCIENCE AND MEDICINE IN VICTORIAN BRITAIN

There was a revolution in science and medicine in Victorian times. It is necessary to pinpoint the landmarks in both disciplines. Although the children cannot be expected to learn them they should be aware of the enormity of the changes that occurred.

SCIENCE

1830s Gas lighting introduced throughout the UK.
1838 First steamship built in England.
1839 William Fox Talbot made photographic prints.
William Cooke and Charles Wheatstone invented the first railway telegraph.
1840 Locomotives began carrying goods and passengers.
1848 Lord Kelvin found the lowest theoretically possible temperature (0°Absolute).
1851 Isaac Merritt Singer invented the first sewing machine.
1859 Charles Darwin's *Origin of Species* shed new light on animal evolution.
1874 First typewriter invented by Remington in the USA.
1875 Alexander Graham bell invented the telephone.
1877 Thomas Edison invented the phonograph or gramophone.
1879 Joseph Swan invented the electric light bulb.
1884 Carl Benz and Gottlieb Daimler built petrol-driven 'horseless carriages' - the motor car.
1899 Guglielmo Marconi sent the first wireless message - the beginning of radio.

MEDICINE

1818 Michael Faraday demonstrated ether stopped people feeling pain.
1819 Laennec invented the stethoscope.
1835 Bequerel and Bruschet first used the clinical thermometer.
1847 James Simpson used chloroform as an anaesthetic.
1847 In Vienna, Semmelweiss suggested surgeon's hands should be washed in chlorinated water before operating.
1861 Florence Nightingale set up a training school for nurses in London.
1870 Louis Pasteur and Robert Koch developed the science of bacteriology.
1871 Joseph Lister introduced his antiseptic spray and outlined the importance of antiseptic surgery.
1885 Louis Pasteur discovered a cure for hydrophobia.
1885 The German scientist Röntgen discovered X-rays.
1899 Vaccination against diptheria successful.
1911 Vitamins discovered.
1928 Alexander Fleming discoverd penicillin.
1935 Sulphonamides, a group of new drugs, discovered.

Pupils should know about these major developments in science and medicine and how they improved public health. Infant mortality declined and people began to live longer. Discuss the problems of a world without heating, sanitation, adequate lighting, the telephone and the radio. Compare and contrast life without these things today. Let the children suggest what they consider to be essential and why.

Discuss the fatal diseases of Victorian times including cholera, tuberculosis, typhus and smallpox. Pinpoint the symptoms and outline the treatment. Outline the developments in hospitals and in public health. Explain how diseases were so easily caught in Victorian times and outline the problems treating them. Use role play as a method of teaching allowing children to be *doctors and nurses*. Devise playlets based on (a) a doctor's surgery in the 19th. century and (b) a doctor's surgery today.

POPULATION

DEATH AND BIRTH RATES

The main Victorian illnesses included tuberculosis, measles, influenza, scarlet fever, cholera, typhoid, smallpox, and gastro-enteritis. In a world without modern drugs like antibiotics, the sulphonamides or even aspirin, many people died young. Many children died before their fifth birthday.

By about 1850 the death rates stabilised at about 22 per 1,000 people until the 1880s and then began to fall again. By the time of Victoria's death it was down to 15 per 1,000. The most striking feature of falling death rates may be seen in the figures on infant mortality. Even as late as 1880, three boys in every 20 and 1 girl in every eight died before they were 1 year old (i.e. 6 boys in 40 and 5 girls in 40). By the 1930s this death rate had almost halved.

POPULATION 1838 - 1911

Year	Population (millions)	Birth rate	Death rate
1838	15.3	30.3	22.4
1841	15.9	32.2	21.6
1851	18.0	34.3	22.0
1861	20.1	34.6	21.6
1871	22.8	35.0	22.6
1881	26.0	33.9	18.9
1891	29.1	31.4	20.2
1901	32.6	28.5	16.9
1911	36.1	24.3	14.6

POPULATION TRENDS - VICTORIAN PERIOD

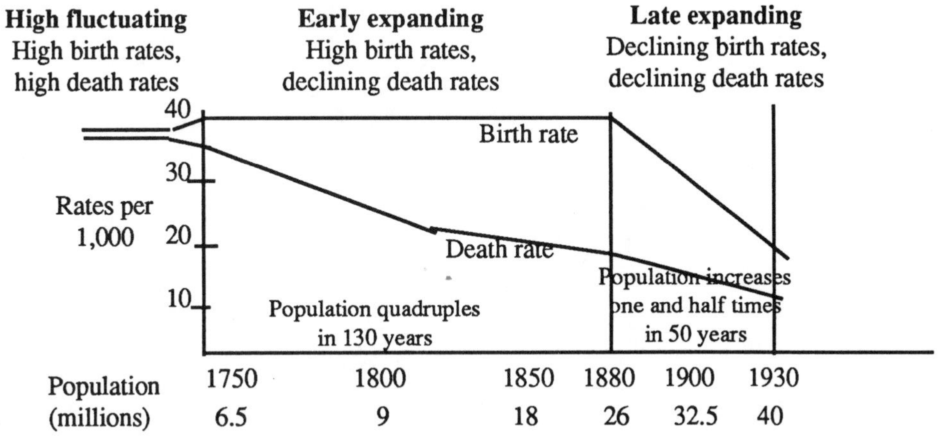

EMIGRATION

The only thing which slowed down population growth in Victorian times was the rise in emigration to such countries as America, Australia, Canada and New Zealand. Between 1871 - 1911, more than 1,952,000 people emigrated.

Discuss the problems arising from the movement of population to the cities. Suggest reasons why children died young and pinpoint the factors which slowed down the death rate - improvements in medical knowledge, surgical operations and post-operative care, the work of the General Medical Council from 1858, improvements in public health, legislation in factories and mines, cheap food imports leading to better diets, improved maternal health and later the certification of midwives. Take the class to a churchyard to find out the ages of those who died at this time.

Discuss emigration and why people wanted to go abroad. Explain why over 90,000 youngsters emigrated during the 60 years 1860 - 1920.

GREAT VICTORIANS

The Victorian period was a time of rapid development in all spheres of life. Many people were involved in these discoveries, inventions and changes and became famous because of their contributions. Research into the lives of a few of these yields much about what it was like to live at this time. The study lends itself to role play. The following list is by no means exhaustive but contains several people worth looking at.

1. Elizabeth Garrett Anderson, first woman doctor.
2. Isabella Beeton, famous Victorian cook (known as Mrs. Beeton).
3. Isambard Kingdom Brunel, famous builder of bridges, tunnels and steamships.
4. Richard Cobden, politician, founder of the Anti-Corn Law League.
5. Charles Dickens, author and novelist.
6. Charles Darwin, naturalist and author.
7. George Eliot, really Mary Ann Evans, author - novelist.
8. William Gladstone, politician.
9. W. G. Grace, all-round cricketer.
10. Thomas Hardy, author - novelist and poet.
11. Octavia Hill, social reformer. Founded the National Trust.
12. Mary Kingsley, naturalist.
13. Joseph Lister, Scottish surgeon - antiseptics.
14. David Livingstone, missionary and explorer.
15. William Lamb, Lord Melbourne, politician.
16. Florence Nightingale, founder of modern nursing.
17. Henry John Temple, Lord Palmerston, politician.
18. Charles Stewart Parnell, Irish politician - Home Rule for Ireland.
19. Robert Peel, politician. Founder of police force (peelers).
20. Robert Gascoyne, Lord Salisbury, politician.
21. Anthony Ashley Cooper, Lord Shaftesbury, social reformer who helped the poor.
22. Robert Louis Stevenson, author of children's books.
23. Alfred, Lord Tennyson, Victorian poet.
24. Edwin Chadwick, social reformer. Reported on Public Health (1842).
25. William Booth founded the Salvation Army.
26. William Fox Talbot, photographic prints.
27. William Cooke and Charles Wheatstone, first railway telegraph.
28. Lord Kelvin, scientist found the lowest temperature theoretically possible (0°A or -273 °C) - still not reached.
29. Alexander Graham Bell invented the telephone.
30. Joseph Swan invented the light bulb.
31. Guglielmo Marconi invented the radio.
32. James Simpson, scientist who made chloroform.
33. Henry Bessemer, engineering scientist who improved the production of steel - including the Bessemer Converter.
34. Alexander Parkes made the first plastics.
35. William Perkins made the first artificial dyes.
36. William Siemens developed steel making.
37. Henry Norton Stanley, explorer.
38. John Hanning Speke, explorer.
39. Alfred Wallace, explorer.
40. Richard Burton, explorer.
41. William Palgrave, explorer.
42. Samuel Baker and Florence Baker, explorers.
43. Edward Whymper, explorer/climber.
44. Sir Francis Edward Younghusband, explorer.
45. Sir John Franklin, sea explorer.
46. Benjamin Disraeli, politician.
47. General Charles Gordon, soldier.
48. Prince Albert, Queen Victoria's consort.
49. Elizabeth Fry, social reformer - prisons.
50. Annie Besant, trade union leader.
51. Dr. Barnardo, social reformer - homes for orphans.
52. Robert Owen, philanthropist, social reformer.
53. Mary Seacole, social reformer - nursing.
54. Thomas Lipton, grocer - Lipton's Stores.
55. Isaac Pitman, inventor - Pitman's shorthand.
56. Charles Kingsley, author - children's books.
57. Anne, Emily and Charlotte Brontë, authors.
58. Lewis Carroll, author of children's books.
59. Anna Sewell, author of children's books.
60. Rudyard Kipling, author - adult's and children's books.
61. Edward Lear, author.
62. James Kay Shuttleworth, reformer - education.
63. Matthew Arnold, poet.
64. Maria Montessori, educationalist.
65. Edward Jenner, doctor - vaccination against smallpox.
66. Karl Benz, inventor - motor car.
67. Gottlieb Daimler, inventor - motor car.
68. John McAdam, road builder.
69. Isaac Merritt Singer, inventor - sewing machine.
70. George Stephenson, inventor - locomotives.
71. William Armstrong, inventor - guns.
72. Lord Kitchener, soldier.
73. William Morris, designer.
74. Thomas Cook, businessman, travel and package holidays.
75. Sir Henry Irving, actor.
76. Edmund Keane, actor.
77. Ellen Terry, actress.
78. James Stanley, inventor - penny farthing.
79. Dr. William, Co-operative retail stores.
80. William Lovett, Chartist movement.
81. Francis Place, Chartist movement.
82. William Symington, ships.
83. Henry Bell, ships.
84. John Elder, ships, compound engine.
85. Sir Charles Parsons, ships, steam turbine.
86. J. B. Dunlop, pneumatic tyres.
87. Rowland Hill, penny post.
88. John Metcalfe, roads.
89. Thomas Telford, roads.
90. John Loudon McAdam, roads.
91. James Watt, steam power.
92. George Stephenson, railways.
93. Robert Browning, poet.
94. John Gibson, architect.
95. Sir John Everett Millais, artist.
96. Thomas Arnold, educationalist.
97. Thomas Carlyle, essayist.
98. Sir John Herschel, astronomer.
99. Frances Trollope, writer and novelist.
100. Elizabeth Barrett Browning, poet.

ADDITIONAL TEACHING IDEAS AND STRATEGIES THE VICTORIANS

This book contains opportunities to give your pupils an insight into **historical concepts.** These embrace time, especially **chronological time:** the value of **historical evidence:** the **importance of changes,** especially on social life and **causes** and **results of historical movements. Similarities** and **differences** are also emphasized and the contributions of **individuals** to history are also important. Students need to learn **historical skills** and to sharpen these as they proceed with their studies. **Providing the evidence** is part of a teacher's work. Children have to learn to **interpret** this whether it is from original or secondary sources. They have to learn to make the appropriate **assumptions** and **deductions. Sequencing** and **observation** are also important historical skills. Students also have to learn how to **communicate** and **record** what they have learned.

Finally, they have to develop an enquiring mind. They need to know that there might be different attitudes to historical movements and developments. Also, history cannot be studied in a vacuum: geography, science, music, art, mathematics, technology and other specialisms have a bearing upon it. Students must learn that there are such things as conflicting evidence or inconclusive or incomplete evidence. They also have to develop a feeling for the past - an empathy if you like - which is often difficult to cultivate in the young child. It is hoped that these additional notes will help to do all this and to show that history has an extra-curricular aspect second to none.

DISCUSSION Techniques include question and answer; debate; stories in miniature; contrasts and similarities with today; a day in the life of a ...; using a film, tape or radio play to start the discussion; using a passage from Dickens, the Brontes or other novel to start discussion.

MATHEMATICS This is most relevant to places. Pose the questions on any Victorian building, place or object *What is it ?What was it used for? How many were there? How old is it? When was it made or built? How much did it cost?* Begin with objects.

SCIENCE Science is concerned with asking questions and finding out. This is especially relevant to the historical environment. Again the questions *how? why?* and *when?* are relevant. As far as the Victorians are concerned, consider the influence of humans on the historic environment - scientific discoveries are important here. Consider Victorian Diet, comparative diets. *What is a balanced diet? How did the Victorians fare?* The Victorians saw the beginning of many scientific inventions and discoveries which influenced the way people lived. Communication, sources of energy, transport, medicine, technology ... these continue to develop at an ever increasing pace today. Consider the importance of the Victorian contribution.

ROLE PLAY This can be used instead of reading or looking at material. Pupils take on the persona of people from the past. They can learn about a character, an event or a place: a Victorian school girl or boy, a Victorian schoolroom, a Victorian school day, a Victorian country house, servant, the squire and his lady, life in a factory, a day in the life of a chimney sweep or a factory worker or a day in the life of a child working a mine.

USING PORTRAITS A portrait is a piece of work (painting, drawing or similar art-work) for which the subject consciously posed. Much can be learned from these but children need 'clues' and practice. Consider costume, colour, jewellery, armour and weapons. Other factors to consider are facial expression and pose, background and accessories. Begin with simple examples and a questionnaire. Queen Victoria and her family or Queen Victoria alone are good starting examples for younger children.

STORYTELLING Young children love to be told a story. It is often a good idea to start or finish a lesson with a story. There are many books full of good stories and material, e.g. *The Story of Steam, Brunel the Shipbuilder, Florence Nightingale and the Beginning of Nursing, Suffragettes and Women's Rights, The Charge of the Light Brigade, The Story of Rorke's Drift ...* A visit to a historical site can be the basis for many stories.

USING VICTORIAN HOUSES/LISTED BUILDINGS A historic house is any building used in the past as a home or built for that purpose. They are still pictures of the past. Children can absorb the past. They can look at the size of the rooms, the kind and arrangement of furniture, where people cooked, ate and slept, discover the lives of those who lived upstairs and downstairs. Find out who looks after the building today. (See Visiting Historical Sites.)

LEARNING FROM OBJECTS Using these is a very important teaching strategy. Children need to examine the object if possible and note its physical features, how it was made, what it is made of, its functions, its design and value. Children can bring things to school but be sure they have permission and that the objects are kept safe. Use Victorian objects as puzzles and point out similarities and differences with items used today. Suitable objects include an old school desk, a blackboard, chalk, a slate, a school bell, a dunce's cap, pen and ink, an abacus, a skipping rope, a candle and holder, an old vacuum cleaner, an old kettle, a washing basin and jug, an old sealer, an egg beater, an old iron and an old scales. Domestic utensils are often very interesting and children marvel at *how things were done.*

USING PHOTOGRAPHS Fortunately for us, photography was invented in Victorian times. Many of these early pictures were posed. (There was little alternative. There were no 'fast films' and photographs took several minutes to develop on the photographic plates.) Children should be aware of this. Victorians loved to have their photographs taken and these were incorporated into jewellery, porcelain and glassware. These photographs are important primary historical sources. Children may be able to bring photographs from home. These are likely to be very fragile. Compare them with written evidence and look at them through a magnifying glass. Turn it into a game - hunting for evidence asking the questions *who? why? when? how?* and *where?* Use 'Now and Then' techniques. Photographs can come from many sources - illustrated books, topographic and travel albums, family albums, old magazines (e.g. *Illustrated London News*) and old newspapers. Family albums give an insight into Victorian domesticity, customs and entertainment. Compare photographs used in Victorian advertising with photographs in promotions today.

USING POSTCARDS, BIRTHDAY CARDS/CHRISTMAS CARDS
These may be useful and the children can handle them, see how they were made and talk about how they were used. Note how elaborate they were - suggest reasons for this. Contrast this presentation with the simplicity of the message - in postcards and greeting cards.

USING ADVERTISEMENTS
Compare Victorian advertisements with today's. Today's assume that the readers are well informed and have a common culture/experience and can understand implied references. Victorian advertisements could not make these assumptions and were more direct and less sophisticated. Use advertisements from Victorian newspapers and place them beside modern examples for comment and discussion.

DRAMA Besides role play, drama is another useful teaching strategy. This can start as a Victorian 'Charades' kind of game, then 'What's My Line' and finally a full dramatic scene. Here are some ideas.

1. An Old Time Music Hall. Create the atmosphere for the event - the children are performers and audience.
2. A Drama Downstairs. A Victorian episode with servants, butler, footman, chauffeur, cook, gardener and ladies' maids ...
3. A Drama Upstairs with Lord and Lady and their snooty children.
4. A drama set in a Victorian schoolroom.
5. A drama set in a Victorian factory.
6. A drama set in a Victorian mine.
7. A child's birthday - a poor family.
8. A child's birthday - a wealthy family.
9. A parody of Fagin - street thieves and their den.
10. An interview with an important person who lived in Victorian times. If possible use a tape recorder or video camera.

USING GEOGRAPHY The factors of location, accessibility to raw materials and skilled people, the resources needed to manufacture goods and how the products were marketed are all important. Victorian industrial sites are interesting to study. Consider where and why particular industries flourished. The children need to mark them on a map and again ask *when? why? who? how?* Let them consider the problems of industrialisation and industrial growth and why some industries have disappeared or moved.

USING TOWN TRAILS
There is so much that is Victorian still around that these can be prepared easily. Look at old maps, newspapers and guide books. Pick out Victorian features including buildings such as churches, factories, markets, town halls, and so on. Also, look for 19th century features - street names, monuments, street lamps, clocks, pillar boxes, pub signs, business signs ... Play 'I Spy Victorian'.

USING FAMILY AND DOMESTIC LIFE It is helpful to ask what was meant by a family in Victorian times - today the family varies from the one parent family to the extended family. Discuss school, church, neighbourhood, village, town, city, nation and world as 'families'. The children can draw their own family trees starting with grandparents. Discuss where they fit into the family. Trace family histories through photographs or albums. If the school is an old one, a school history might be appropriate.

Compare and contrast family life in Victorian times with today. Use a 'Then' and 'Now' chart. Compare domestic arrangements. Illustrate with reference to servants, the aged and the young. Discuss the changes in housing - own bedroom, bathrooms, flush toilets, soap and water, toothpaste and so on. [It may be advisable to discuss a general Victorian family and a general family today rather than private details of the families of the children.]

USING DIET AND COOKING Use Mrs Beeton's Cookery Book as a start and discussVictorian diet. Discuss how the poor fared and what childhood diseases existed because of deficiencies in the diet, especially of the poor. Compare the diet of a labourer with that of a gentleman, a factory worker with that of a factory owner. Discuss the importance of the price of bread. Explain the role of potatoes in diet and the social and political consequences of the potato famine in Ireland. Compare Victorian diet with children's diet today. Is today's diet better and if so, why? Is today's diet as good as it should be? If not, why not? Discuss differences in cooking methods and the preservation of food. Explain why large kitchens and staff were needed - virtually everything had to be made at home.

VICTORIAN LITERATURE, ART AND ENTERTAINMENT Let the children research Victorian authors. They may make monographs with photographs or drawings, life histories and brief details of what they wrote. Let them dip into Victorian stories and say why they like or dislike them. Excerpts from Victorian authors, especially those with historical or social themes give an insight into Victorian life. Always ask for comments and where possible compare and contrast pieces of work by the same author or by different writers. Humorous pieces are also important, for example the work of Robert Smith Surtees (1803 - 1864). *Punch* is also useful. Children might design a Victorian book or file cover for their work. Explain the absence of colour photogrpahs and illustrations and why there are only a few photographs in Victorian books. They might write a short piece of prose on 'Life in a Victorian Village' or town or city or 'Life in a Victorian School'. A child could pretend to a journalist and write an article on 'A Victorian Christmas'.

Plan a visit to an art gallery which has a display of Victorian work. The children can compare and contrast with today's art and look for the Japanese influence in some of the Victorian work. Mention the pre-Raphaelitites and the work of William Morris. Let them make a sampler or work together on patchwork. Encourage the children to copy a Victorian illustration or draw one like it and use it in a birthday or other greetings card.

Victorians made their own entertainment. Compare with the situation today. Play Victorian games especially charades with the children. The children might like to make moving pictures. The Victorians understood how to make things appear to move, the beginning of cinema, but did not have the technology to do it.

Take the children to an olde tyme music hall or help them to organise one for themselves. Photocopy some famous scenes from Victorian novels and the children can act out the various roles and events. The children might act out a meeting between a famous person such as Queen Victoria, Robert Louis Stevenson or Disraeli. It is more fun if the children dress up.

MOVING PICTURES

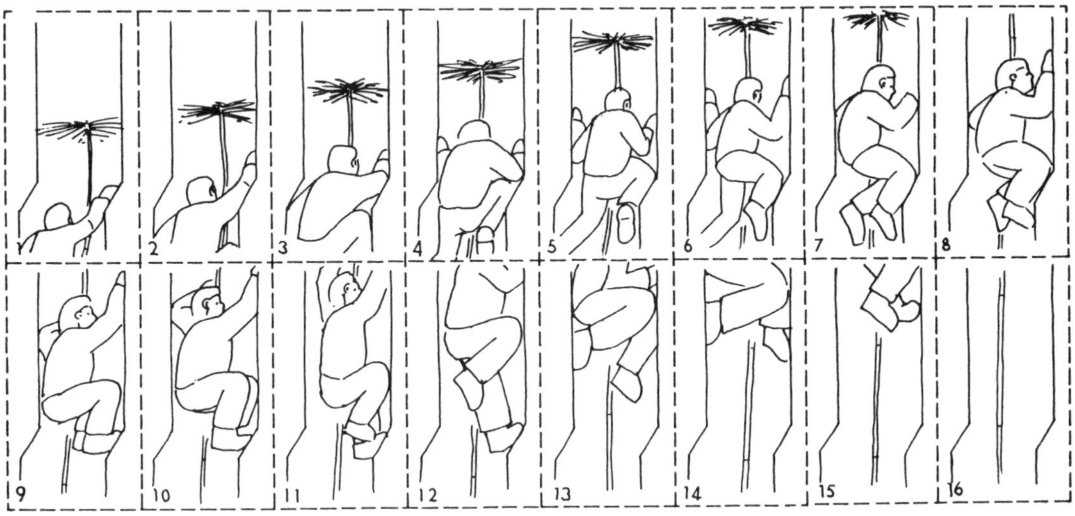

The Disappearing Chimney Sweep

Cut out strips of paper 8 cm long and the same height as the little pictures. Cut out the pictures and paste them in order on to the right hand ends of the strips with number 1 on the top strip and number 16 on the bottom. Staple the strips together on the left hand side and flick through them to make a moving picture. Now make your own set of drawings. This is the basis of animation today.

VISITING HISTORICAL SITES

THE IMPORTANCE OF VISITS

A visit to a Victorian site or a museum brings the threads of the study together. 'Chalk and talk' are now turned into reality. Pupils can see for themselves where the Victorians lived and 'seeing is believing'. Observation is the keynote but there may be possibilities of participation in the Victorian way of life and of role play. Fortunately, throughout Britain there are many Victorian sites and excellent museum displays. Try to visit the chosen site alone before taking a group or class.

PREPARATION FOR A SITE VISIT

BEFORE THE VISIT

Choose a site that is appropriate and can be easily reached or preferably is near to the school. Make a list of the reasons for and the aims of the visit. Decide which National Curriculum topics are to be covered and which targets you wish to meet. If possible visit the site yourself before you take the class. Most sites have teachers' notes and worksheets which are usually helpful and save a great deal of time. You may wish to modify them to suit your class and your own objectives. It is very important to prepare the children for the visit. The site will seem exciting and strange to them when they arrive. They may wander off aimlessly, waste time and possibly get into dangerous situations.

Decide what you are going to tell the children about the site before the visit. Few are likely to be born historians and they need enough information to enable them to understand what they will see during the visit. Slides, photographs, ground/site plans are helpful beforehand if they are available. It may be useful to talk about Victorian sites in general and then discuss the site you are planning to visit in particular. One visit is not going to cover everything and so decide exactly what you want to concentrate on. Depending on the age and abilities of the children, keep it short and keep it simple. Above all, they should enjoy it educationally and socially.

It may be necessary to enhance the children's visual skills. The visit may involve using the following skills at some level.

1. Observation skills.
2. Recording skills.
3. Being able to make comparisons.
4. Being able to make deductions.
5. Reading, writing and comprehension skills.
6. Measuring skills.
7. Estimating skills.
8. The ability to read maps.
9. The ability to read plans.
10. Mathematical skills.
11. Scientific skills.
12. Social skills, especially sharing and communicating.

A sense of time may be learned from the site and youngsters may realise the importance of historical evidence. Aesthetically, the group may gain a great deal from what they see. Pupils need guidance about the information and data they can gather at the site. Practise by organising a survey of the school, school grounds, village or an area of a town before the visit. This should be simple but it is helpful to observe a familiar place closely and discover the relationship between information on a flat piece of paper like a map or diagram drawn by the pupil and the 3D environment.

Devise your own activity pack for use on the site. This should include illustrations, a questionnaire and questions requiring observation and deduction.

TEACHERS' CHECK LIST

On your personal visit before taking your group or class consider the following.

1. Kind of site. Is the site industrial, commercial, residential or other? Is the building decorative or utilitarian or both? If residential, was it the home of wealthy or poor Victorians?

2. Geography of the land. Consider this, the lie of the land and the geology of the site.

3. Location of the site. Why was the site chosen? Does the location have any advantages?

4. Previous occupation of the site. Was the site occupied beforeVictorian times? If so, how did the Victorians change or adapt it?

5. Changes in the site. Has the site been changed or affected by 'modern' developments such as the building of a motorway or housing? If so, what did it look like in Victorian times?

6. Discoveries. Have there been any important discoveries or finds at the site? If so, pinpoint them so that you can discuss them with the children.

7. When was the site used? Was it used in peacetime or wartime or both?

8. Buildings. Consider the buildings. What kinds of homes were they, what was their size and where were they located?

9. Size of the community. Consider the size and social structure of the community associated with the site. Did any important people live in the community? Are there any indications of a farrier, doctor, lawyer, school teacher ... ? Is an author or poet connected with the area?

10. Occupation. What was the occupation of the owner - landowner, mine owner, aristocrat ...?

11. Food. What evidence is there about diet, cooking and cooking utensils? What can be learned about the storage and preparation of food in Victorian times? What size is the kitchen? How is it equipped?

12. Animals. Were animals such as horses or dogs kept on the site?

13. Meat. Is there any evidence of food processing, meat eating or meat cooking?

14. Food preservation. Are there any details of the storage of grain. Was food preserved?

15. Natural resources. What were the natural resources of the site - such as wood, stone, clay or charcoal? Were there any natural resources close by? Have these been exhausted?

16. Skilled work. Is there any evidence of skilled work such as making cloth, leather goods ... ? Were the rooms planned and furnished by someone important? Are the rooms (and the building) finely decorated, e.g. with expensive wood panelling or gold leaf?

17. Grounds. Are the grounds extensive and well laid out? Who planned them and who maintains them now?

18. Metal working. Is there any evidence of metal working (lead, tin, bronze, iron, silver, gold) at the site? Look for equipment, tools, jewellery and artefacts.

19. Other materials. Is there any evidence of the use of stone, shale, slate or other materials on the site? (If so have they been used practically or aesthetically or both?

20. Clothes. Is there any evidence of the production of woollen or linen material and clothes?

21. Women. What did the women do? How do you know?

22. Finds of special interest.

SOME PLACES TO VISIT

Here are some museums and sites of Victorian interest to visit.
Your local Tourist Office will have details of more in your area.
(Also see list of Victorian Schoolrooms in Educational Section.)

Acton Scott Historic Working Farm, Shropshire.
The Argory, County Tyrone, Northern Ireland. Victorian house with a fascinating collection of furniture.
Balmoral Castle, near Ballater, Grampian region.
Biddulph Grange, Stoke-on-Trent. Rare example of a Victorian garden.
Bluebell Line, Horsted Keynes. Working railway with many steam locomotives.
Bodelwyddan Castle, Clwyd. 19th. century castle creation with many Victorian exhibits.
Bronte Parsonage Museum, Haworth, West Yorkshire.
Buckingham Palace, London. Queen Victoria was the first to modernise this famous residence.
Calke Abbey, Derby. Almost unchanged since the last century. Full of everyday Victorian things.
Cardiff Castle, South Glamorgan.
Carlow County Museum, Carlow, Eire. Nineteenth-century Irish exhibits.
Castell Coch, near Cardiff, South Glamorgan.
Castle Ward, Northern Ireland.
Castle Museum, York. Includes a reconstruction of a Victorian parlour.
Charlecote Park, Warwickshire.
Charles Dickens's Birthplace Museum, Portsmouth.
Clifton Suspension Bridge, Bristol, Avon.
Cotehele, St. Dominick, Cornwall.
David Livingstone Centre, Blantyre, Strathclyde.
Dickens' House Museum, Doughty Street, London.
Erddig, Clwyd.
Dunham Massey, Cheshire.
Fox Talbot Museum, Lacock, Wilts. Museum of photography in memory of Fox Talbot who lived there.
Gondola Steam Yacht, Coniston Water, Cumbria. First launched in 1859, still carries sightseers.
Great Britain, Great Western Dock, Bristol Docks. Brunel's great iron steamship.
Florence Court, Northern Ireland.
Great Western Railway Museum, Swindon, Wilts.
Hardy's Cottage, Bockhampton, near Dorchester, Dorset. Birthplace of the great poet and novelist, Thomas Hardy.
Hatfield House, Herts.
Highland Folk Museum, Kingussie, Scotland. Has a copy of a turf-roofed hut lived in by nineteenth century Scots.
High Level Bridge, Newcastle-upon-Tyne.
HMS Warrior, HM Naval Base, Portsmouth.
Hughenden Manor, High Wycombe. Home of Disraeli for over 30 years.
Ironbridge Gorge Museum, Telford, Shropshire.
Kew Bridge Steam Museum, Brentford, Middx.
Knightshayes Court, Tiverton, Devon. House has a richly decorated Victorian interior.
Lanhydrock, Cornwall.
Lyme Park, Cheshire.
Michael Faraday's Laboratory and Museum, The Royal Institution, Albermarle Street, London.
Museum of Childhood, High Street, Edinburgh. Has many Victorian toys and games.
Museum of London, London Wall, London.
Museum of Rural Life, Reading. Has many photographs and tools of Victorian countryside.
National Army Museum, Royal Hospital Road, Chelsea, London.
National Maritime Museum, Romney Road, Greenwich. Magnificent sailing ship *Cutty Sark* moored here.
National Railway Museum, York. Collection of old steam railway engines and rolling stock.
Natural History Museum, London. One of the great, grand museums planned by Prince Albert.
Newport, Gwent. The town has a fine example of a Victorian market building.
North of England Open Air Museum, Beamish, County Durham. Reconstructions include a Victorian school room and a miner's cottage.
Osborne House, Isle of Wight.
Penrhyn Castle, Gwynedd.
Port Sunlight, Merseyside. High quality houses built for factory workers in 1880s.
Quarry Bank Mill, Styal, Cheshire.
Royal Albert Bridge, Saltash, Cornwall.
Royal Museum of Scotland. Main hall based on the design for the Crystal Palace.
St. Gastayn Church, Llangasty, Powys. Church in the 'Gothic Revival' style fashionable in early 1800s.
St. Pancras Station, London.
Science Museum, South Kensington, London.
Shugborough, Staffordshire.
Speke Hall, Merseyside.
Tatton Park, Cheshire.
Welsh Industrial and Maritime Museum, Cardiff. Many relics from the Industrial Revolution.
Victorian and Albert Museum, South Kensington, London.
Victoria Square, Birmingham.
Windsor Castle, Berkshire. Victoria and Albert are buried in the park.
Woburn Abbey, Bedfordshire.
York Castle Museum, Eye of York, York.

AT THE SITE

Make use of the surroundings of the site as well as buildings there. Let the pupils study their surroundings including flora, fauna, trees (include bark rubbings if appropriate), animal habitats and so on. Instead of or as well as the guidance from activity sheets, the children may be asked to solve a problem from the past. Examples are:

You are administrator of this Victorian house. How would you preserve what is there?

Show how this house was organised in Victorian times.

Distinguish between those who lived 'upstairs' and those who lived 'downstairs' in these premises.

A group of foreign tourists who have no previous knowledge of Victorian buildings intends to visit the place. List the main features you would tell them about. Why have you chosen these features?

The children may imagine they are Victorians at the site. Give them roles to play and work out how these roles may be fulfilled. If it is practical, pupils can wear Victorian dress and the site can be used to re-enact an event from history such as the birth of Prince Edward or the preparations for Victoria's Diamond Jubilee. The use of an unfamiliar site in this way may be difficult and not as useful as using role play as part of the follow up.

FOLLOW UP TO A VISIT

To reinforce the visit you might consider the following when you return to the classroom.

1. Devise a quiz to find out how much the children have learned.
2. Devise other written work especially making them see the site as a place where people lived and worked. How did the site operate on a daily basis? Use actual characters from Victorian times if possible.
3. Guide the children to write reports on particular aspects of the site - the Victorian kitchen, the Victorian dining room and so on.
4. Use the activity pack/worksheets/guide book.
5. Organise the pupils to make a display of any written work - drawings, maps, ground plans, photographs ... Develop this for use in the classroom and classify and label any objects. Some children may make models, (some accurately scaled) costumed figures and measured drawings.
6. Pinpoint any technology from the site such as roads, buildings or statues. Spinning, dyeing, weaving and artefacts are part of this.
7. Pinpoint the diet and ways in which food was cooked.
8. Pupils could make a frieze or collage. Brass or other rubbings may be possible.
9. The pupils could write and act a play or situation which might have occurred on the site such as a conversation between a Victorian servant and his/her master.
10. Use slides, drawings, photographs and so on to prepare an audio-visual presentation. Tape-slide sequences, presentations or a video presentation may be possible depending on the site and the age and abilities of the children.
11. Pupils may examine documents (i.e. copies of documents) from the site. They could ask themselves
    When was it written? How do we know when it was written?
    Who wrote it? Why was it written?
    What sort of document is it? (Personal communication, order or command, official or unofficial ...)
    Are there any differences btween this document and others? Compare and contrast the documents if more than one is availble.
    Is it one of a series of documents? How do we know the original is genuine?

Finally, it is necessary to evaluate the visit objectively and write a brief report on how such a visit may be improved next time.

BOOKLIST / RESOURCES

GENERAL REFERENCE BOOKS/PUBLICATIONS

Adams, C.,	*Ordinary Life a Century Ago*, Virago, 1982
Barrett, J.,	*Useful Toil - Autobiographies of Working People from the 1820s to the 1920s*, Allen Lane, 1974
Benson, A. C. and Viscount Esher (eds.),	*The Letters of Queen Victoria 1837 - 1861*, (3 vols.) John Murray, 1908
Briggs, Asa,	*Victorian People*, Penguin, 1965
Ensor, R.C.K.,	*England, 1870 - 1914*, Oxford University Press, 1980
Evans, D.,	*How We Used to Live - Victorians Early and Late*, A. and C. Black, 1990
Harker, M.F.,	*Victorian and Edwardian Photographs*, Charles Letts, 1975
Horn, R.,	*The Victorian and Edwardian School Child*, A. Sutton, 1989
Huggett, F.E.,	*Victorian England as seen by Punch*, Sidgwick and Jackson, 1978
Hyndman, M.,	*Schools and Schooling in England and Wales, a Documentary History*, Harper and Row, 1978
Johnson, E.,	*The Dawn of Motoring*, Mercedes - Benz, UK, 1986
Mayhew, H.,	*London Labour and the London Poor*, (4 vols.) Cass, 1967
Pocock, J.I.,	*The Diary of a London Schoolboy, 1826 - 1830*, Camden History Society, 1980
Rawcliffe, M.,	*Finding out about Victorian London*, Batsford, 1985
Riley, N.,	*Victorian Design Source Book*, Phaidon 1989
Strachey, Lytton,	*Eminent Victorians*, Penguin, 1948
Thomson, D.,	*England in the Nineteenth Century*, Penguin, 1950
Ward, J.I.,	*The Age of Change 1770 - 1970 - Documentts in Social History*, Adam and Charles Black, 1975
Woodham-Smith, C.,	*Florence Nightingale 1820 - 1910*, Constable, 1950

VICTORIAN WRITERS (For Children) Any Edition

Barrie, J.M.,	*Peter Pan*
Browning, R.,	*The Pied Piper of Hamelin*
Caroll, Lewis,	*Alice's Adventures in Wonderland* and *Through the Looking Glass*
Dickens, Charles,	*Oliver Twist, David Copperfield, Great Expectations* and *A Christmas Carol*
Kingsley, Charles,	*The Water Babies, Westward Ho*
Kipling, Rudyard,	*The Jungle Book, Just So Stories*
Nesbit, Edith,	*The Railway Children, Five Children and It*
Potter, Beatrix.,	*The Tale of Peter Rabbit*
Stevenson, R.L.,	*Treasure Island, Kidnapped*
Sewell, Anna,	*Black Beauty*

ORIGINAL SOURCES

Besides the source books mentioned in the general list above, teachers are advised to consult the numerous parliamentary papers and reports published throughout the period. School material can be found in written records such as log books, attendance registers, punishment books and the reports of HM Inspectors. [Such records dating from the middle of the 19th. century may be found in the schools themselves, in local and county record offices and the Public Record Office at Kew.] Also, numerous newspapers and magazines relating to the Victorian period are available in most reference libraries.

PUPILS' RESOURCES - WORKSHEETS

THE YOUNG QUEEN

1. This drawing shows Victoria learning about her accession. What was the date?

2. How old was Victoria when she became Queen?

3. Name the Queen's uncle who had died.

4. Name the ministers in the picture.

5. Choose one word from the following to indicate Victoria's reaction to succeeding to the throne:

RESIGNED DUTIFUL TRUSTWORTHY SHATTERED ANNOYED

QUEEN VICTORIA

1. Fill in the spaces in this genealogical table relating to Queen Victoria.

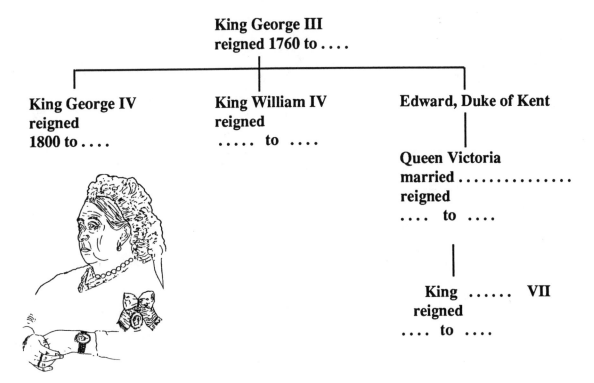

King George III
reigned 1760 to . . . .

King George IV
reigned
1800 to . . . .

King William IV
reigned
. . . . . to . . . .

Edward, Duke of Kent

Queen Victoria
married . . . .
reigned
. . . . to . . . .

King VII
reigned
. . . . to . . . .

2. Complete this time-line of important events in Queen Victoria's life. The first one has been done for you.

1819 Birth of Victoria.

1837

1840

1861

1876

1887

1897

1901

3. What was Victoria's nickname when she was a young girl?

4. What was Victoria's nickname after the death of Albert?

5. How long did Victoria reign?

THE TIMES NEWSPAPER 1837

THE QUEEN'S CORONATION

You are a reporter on the *The Times* and you have been commissioned to write an eye witness account of the coronation of Queen Victoria in 1837. You should write your report in the first person singular (begin 'I am at Westminster Abbey ...'). The drawing below will help you.

VICTORIAN TIMES

These are drawings of objects used in Victorian times. Write what they are below each drawing. On a separate sheet of paper, draw objects that might be used in their place today.

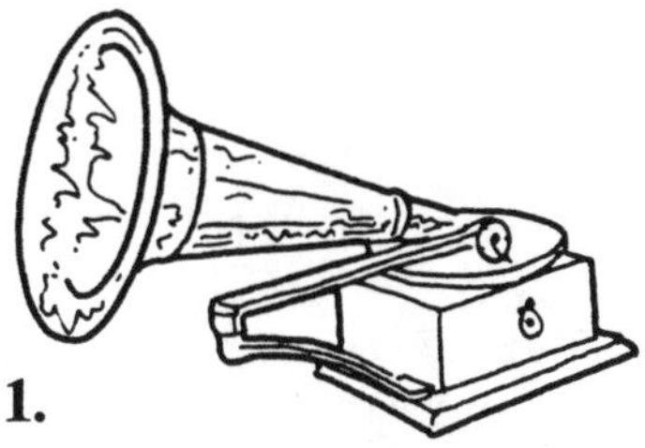

1. ______________________

2. ______________________

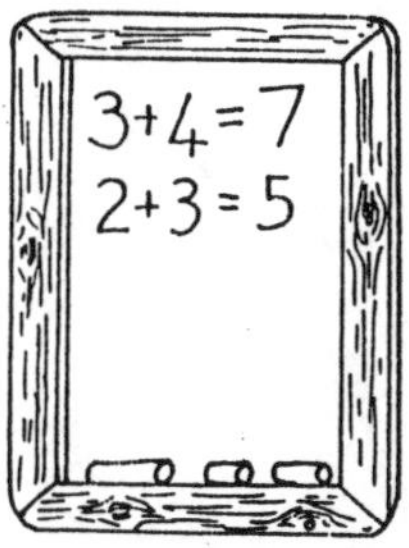

3. ______________________

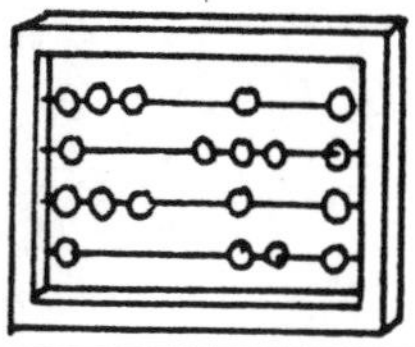

4. ______________________

5. ______________________

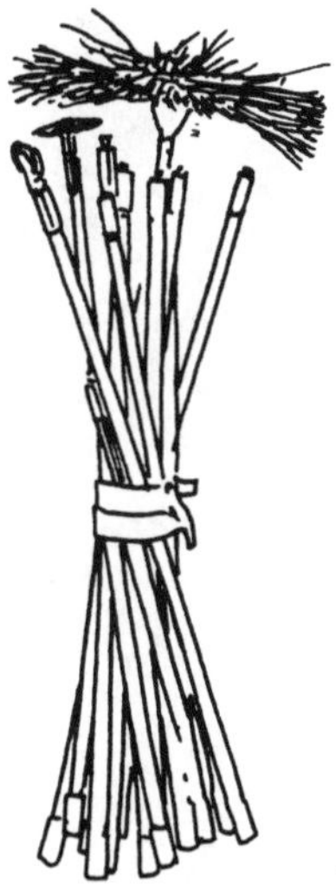

6. ______________________

7. ______________________

8. ______________________

9. ______________________

10. ______________________

FLORENCE NIGHTINGALE

1. This is a drawing of Florence Nightingale helping wounded soldiers at the hospital at Scutari. Colour it and write an account of her life and work.

2. Below is a letter written by Queen Victoria to Florence Nightingale. Read it carefully and then answer the questions which follow it.

WINDSOR CASTLE, (January, 1856)

DEAR Miss Nightingale You are, I know, well aware of the high sense I entertain of the Christian devotion which you have displayed during this great and bloody war, and I need hardly repeat to you how warm my admiration is for your services, which are fully equal to those of my dear and brave soldiers, whose sufferings you have had the privilege of alleviating in so merciful a manner. I am, however, anxious of marking my feelings in a manner which I trust will be agreeable to you, and therefore send you with this letter a brooch, the form and emblems of which commemorate your great and blessed work, and which, I hope, you will wear as a mark of the high approbation of your Sovereign!

It will be a very great satisfaction to me, when you return at last to these shores, to make the acquaintance of one who has set so bright an example to our sex. And with every prayer for the preservation of your valuable health, believe me, always, yours sincerely,

VICTORIA R.

1. Is this letter a primary or secondary source? Give reasons for your answer.
2.'... this great and bloody war ...' [line 2]. What war does this refer to? Who took part in the war?
3. Where was Florence Nightingale when she received this letter from the Queen and what had she done?
4. Complete the following.
Florence Nightingale was known as the lady with the .....
5. Explain the following words 'entertain' (line 1); 'devotion' (line 2) 'admiration' (line 3); 'alleviating' (line 4).
6. According to the passage, what gift did Queen Victoria send Florence Nightingale? Do you think this was an appropriate gift? Give reasons for your answer.
7. Name the Jamaican nurse who helped Florence Nightingale in her work.
8. What career did Florence Nightingale improve for women?
9. What did Florence Nightingale start when she returned to Britain?
10. What was the significance of Florence Nightingale's work for women generally in the 19th. century?

DISRAELI AND INDIA

This illustration from the magazine, *Punch* shows Disraeli holding the key of India.
Look at it carefully and then answer the questions on it.

1. **What had Disraeli done to have such a key? Give the date of the event and name the other party involved.**

2. **Name the structure in the background of the picture. This suggests another country was concerned with the event. Name this country.**

3. **Write a paragraph on the event and say why you think it was a success or failure.**

4. **Why did the event help British trade with India and the Far East?**

5. **Suggest a caption for the picture.**

THE CRIMEAN WAR

This illustration appeared in *Punch* magazine in 1854. Look at it and then answer the questions on it.

A Trump Card

1. **This picture shows one of the biggest disasters of the Crimean War. What was it called and when did it occur?**

2. **Give a brief account of this event, pointing out the main reason for the disaster.**

3. **Why is the caption *A Trump Card* humorous? To whom does it refer?**

4. **Colour the picture and suggest your own title for it.**

5. **What, if anything, does the event tell us about the abilities of army officers at this time?**

A VICTORIAN MAGAZINE

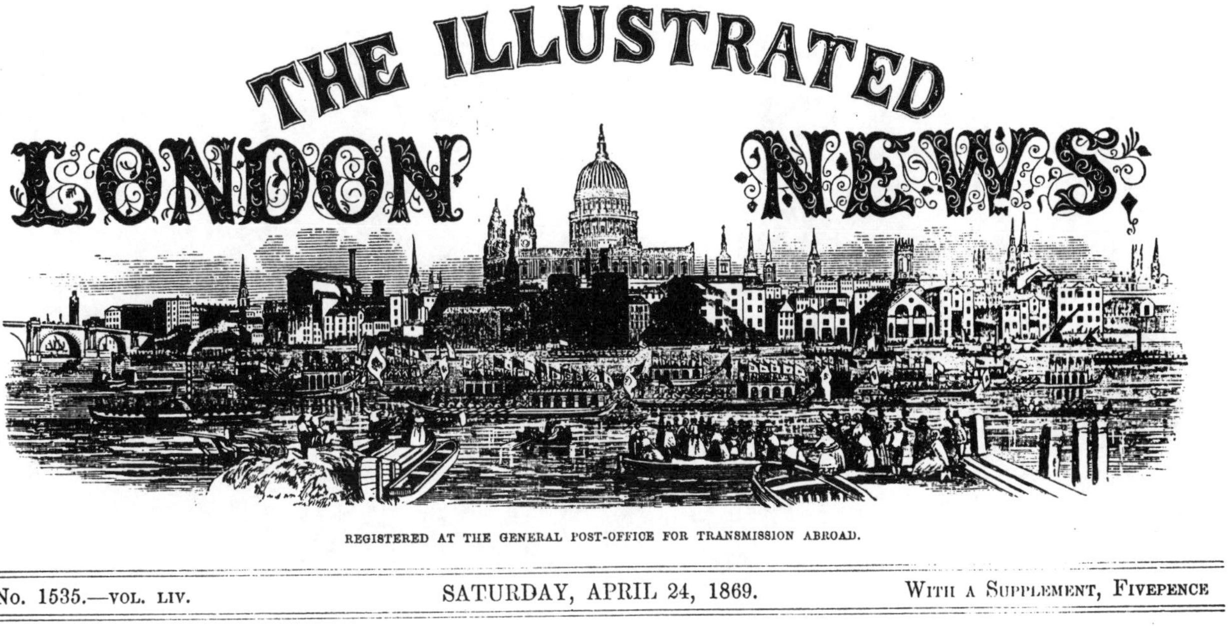

THE ILLUSTRATED LONDON NEWS.

REGISTERED AT THE GENERAL POST-OFFICE FOR TRANSMISSION ABROAD.

No. 1535.—VOL. LIV. SATURDAY, APRIL 24, 1869. WITH A SUPPLEMENT, FIVEPENCE

The picture above is part of the front page of a magazine published in Victoria's Time. Answer these questions on it.

1. When was the magazine published?

2. How much did it cost? What was sold with it for this price?

3. What suggests that this is a Victorian magazine?

4. Is this magazine an original or secondary source?

5. What did publishers in Victorian times have to do before they could sell their magazines overseas?

6. Name the river in front of the buildings.

7. Complete the following by choosing the correct word from the alternatives given 'Most of the vessels were propelled by sail/steam/oarsmen.'

8. Suggest some important differences between this Victorian magazine and one you could buy in a shop today.

THE RAINHILL TRIALS

1. Colour this picture of the Rainhill Trials.
2. What were these trials? Who took part and who was the victor?
3. What were the consequences of the coming of the railways (a) for the transportation of goods and (b) for the stage coach business?

QUEEN VICTORIA'S TRAIN

Queen's Victoria's Railway Carriage and Locomotive

The carriage, built of double-panelled mahogany, was 13 feet long and 7 feet wide. Felt was packed between the wooden panels to lessen vibrations and to keep the carriage warm inside. The inside of the carriage was lined with padded blue satin with matching curtains. Ventilation was through the dome in the roof.

1. This drawing shows Queen Victoria's own carriage and locomotive. What does it show about locomotive developments at this time?
2. What do you understand by 'railway mania'?
3. Who or what were 'navvies'?
4. What was the first modern public railway to provide steam-hauled trains for passengers?

THE REBECCA RIOTS

1. When did these riots occur? What were the rioters protesting against?

2. Where did they occur? Had there been any similar disturbances before? If so, give an example.

3. Did the attacks take place in the day or at night and what did the rioters do?

4. What sex were 'Rebecca' and 'her daughters'? It is said that the name Rebecca was a biblical reference. Give the reference.

5. What is the building in the top right corner of the page called?

6. 'The riots were really a response to wider social dissatisfaction than road problems.' Explain this statement.

7. How did the government deal with the rioters at first?

8. In 1844, government legislation improved the situation. Explain why.

THE 'HORSELESS CARRIAGE'

Anne Hathaway's Cottage.
"Silence is the perfectest Herald of Joy."—Shakespeare.
The Talbot is the perfectest Herald of Silence.
Catalogue, Specifications, and full Particulars from
CLEMENT TALBOT, Ltd., Automobile Engineers, Barlby Road, N. Kensington, W.
Telephone: 5006 Paddington (4 lines). Telegrams: "Clemtal, London."

This is an early advertisement adapted from a Victorian newspaper (1870).

1. What is meant by a 'horseless carriage'?

2. Name the item being advertised.

3. What had to proceed such vehicles at this time? Why was this necessary?

4. *The 'horseless carriage' had taken over from horses by the end of Victoria's time.* True or false?

5. What were the main disadvantages of these early vehicles? Who (that is what class of person) bought them when they were first made?

6. Name two inventors of the 'horseless carriage'? What did British inventors contribute, if anything?

7. Is the scene in the drawing set in the town or country? Give reasons for your answer.

8. Compare and contrast this Victorian vehicle with a modern car.

9. Explain what is meant by the following words under the drawing: 'catalogue', 'specifications' and '4 lines'.

DAIMLER 1899

This is a drawing of the 12 horse-power Daimler of 1899, one of the first cars to be built in Britain under licence from the German inventor, Gottlieb Daimler. Look at the drawing and then answer the questions that follow it.

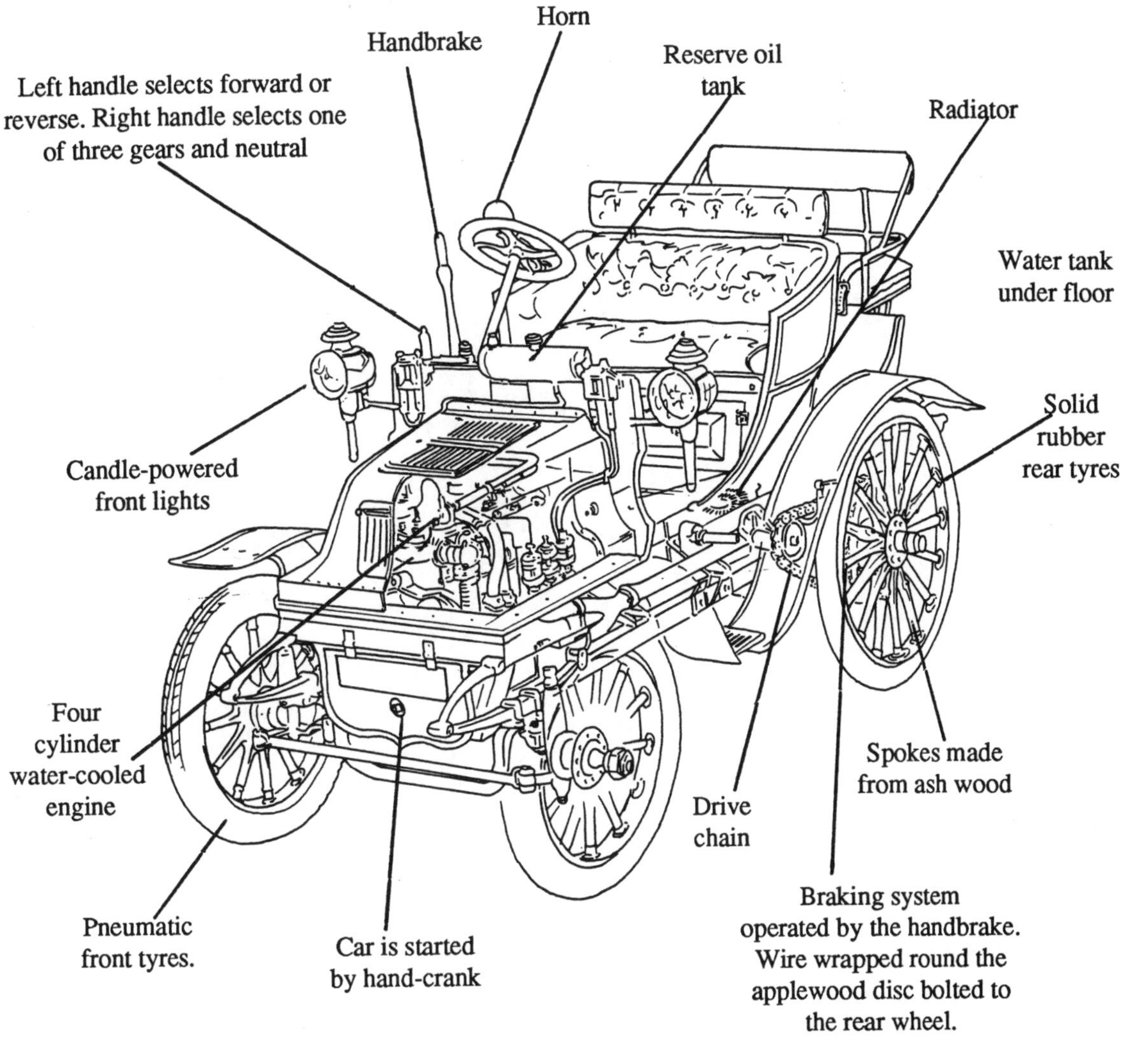

1. **What is meant by a 'hand crank to start the car'? How are cars started today?**
2. **What are 'candle-powered lights'? Would they have made driving in the dark easy? Give reasons for your answer.**
3. **What were the spokes of the wheels made of? Compare the tyres on the back and front wheels. What is the meaning of 'pneumatic'?**
4. **How many gear handles did the Daimler have? How many gear handles do cars have today?**
5. **What was the braking system? What transmits stopping force in modern cars?**
6. **Where is the radiator in this Daimler? Where is the radiator usually in today's cars?**
7. **There is a reserve oil tank. What does this suggest about its oil consumption?**
8. **Queen Victoria described early 'horseless carriages' as *disagreeable conveyances altogether - they smell, are exceedingly nasty and are very shaky.* Would you have agreed with her at the time? Give reasons for your answer.**
9. ***This Daimler is a miracle of engineering and ingenuity.* Say, with reasons, if you think this is true.**
10. **Suppose you were going to travel in this Daimler in 1899, what preparations would you have had to make about clothes, weather, fuel, length of journey and so on?**

CLASS IN VICTORIAN TIMES

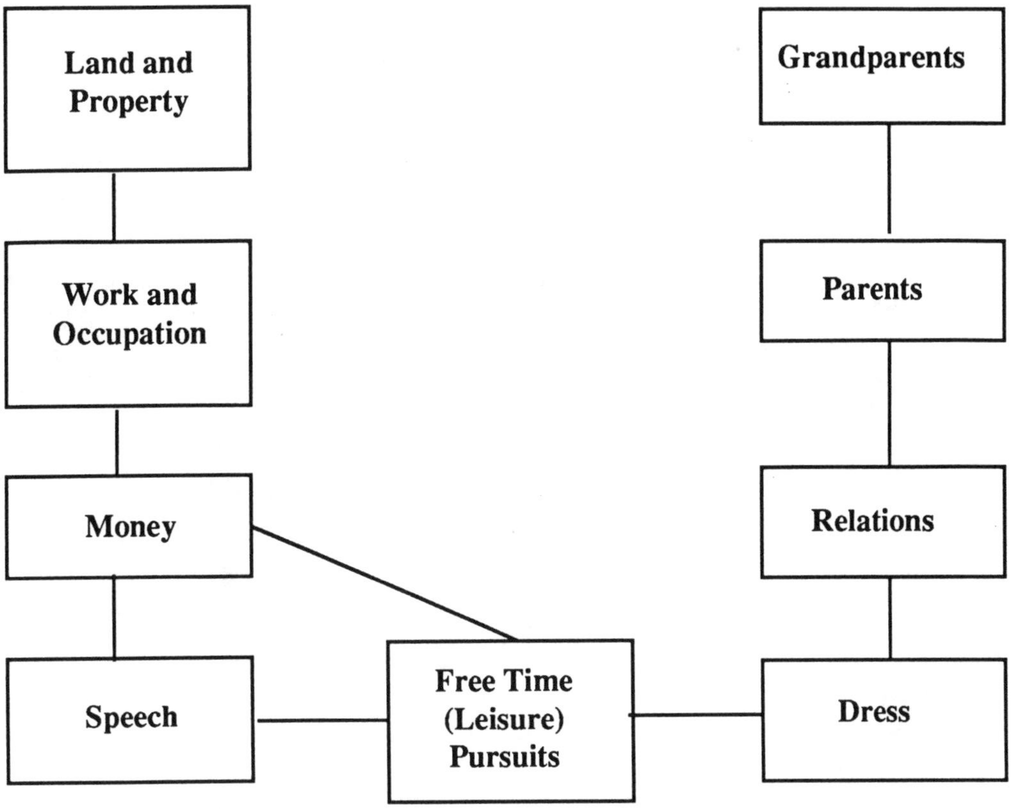

1. Consider these factors in deciding which class in society people belonged to in Victorian times. Which factors were most important?

2. Explain what was meant by upper class, middle class and working class in Victorian times.

3. To which class did the following belong?
   (a) factory worker, (b) doctor, (c) governess, (d) landowner, (e) lady's maid, (f) carpenter, (g) shop owner, (h) banker, (i) miner, (j) lawyer.

4. Describe a day in the life of (a) a young working class girl and (b) a young upper class lady.

5. Outline the differences in the education or training of a working class young man and an upper class young man.

6. Do you think that 'class' exists in society today? If so, how important is it? Give reasons for your answers.

CLASS IN VICTORIAN TIMES

THE GREAT EXHIBITION, 1851

1. When did the Great Exhibition take place?

2. Whose idea was the Great Exhibition?

3. The Exhibition building was designed by the talented head gardener/architect of Chatsworth House. Name him.

4. What was the Exhibition structure called?

5. Give three details about the Exhibition building.

6. What was the purpose of the Exhibition?

7. How many exhibitors took part altogether? Give the numbers of (a) British and (b) foreign businesses which took part.

8. How many people visited the Exhibition?

9. 'The Great Exhibition was very successful.' True or false'? Give reasons for your answer.

10. When was the Exhibition building removed, where was it rebuilt and what happened to it in the end?

SHOPPING

A

B

1. Which drawing shows shopping in Victorian times?
2. Which shop is easier to use from the point of view of choosing goods?
3. Picture 1 has two chairs for customers. Give one reason for having these. What are the disadvantages? Modern shops do not have chairs like this, what do they sometimes have instead?
4. In Picture A, many of the goods are on the counter, unwrapped. What are your views on this?
5. Two words can be used to describe the service in these shops: personal and impersonal. Which do you think would offer you a personal service and which would offer an impersonal service?
6. There is a clock in the Victorian shop. Most modern shops do not have clocks. Suggest a reason for this.
7. Why is music played in some large modern stores? Would music have been played in Victorian shops? Give reasons for your answer.
8. What essential shopping aid is provided in today's supermarkets that was not available in Victorian shops?
9. Compare shopping in Victorian times with shopping today. Which would you prefer? Give reasons for your answer.

FAMOUS VICTORIANS

The following are drawings of some famous Victorians followed by a list of their actions, achievements, records, inventions, writings or works of art. Write the correct caption under each drawing. The first one has been done for you.

WILLIAM BOOTH

Founded Salvation Army

CHARLES DARWIN

WILLIAM IV

DISRAELI

LEWIS CARROLL

GLADSTONE

DR. W. G. GRACE

LORD SHAFTESBURY

CHARLES DICKENS

DAVID LIVINGSTONE

CAPTIONS

Author of *The Origin of Species.*
Founded Salvation Army.
Liberal Politician.
Tory Politician.
Queen Victoria's Uncle.
Author of *Alice in Wonderland.*
Famous African Explorer.
Famous Sportsman (Cricketer).
Prison Reformer.
Wrote *Oliver Twist.*

A VICTORIAN DICTIONARY QUIZ

Fill in the boxes

MEANING	WORD
1. A drug which puts patients to sleep.	1.
2. Describes two rows of houses with their backs closely facing each other.	2.
3. United Kingdom and territories world wide once under its control.	3.
4. Official record of the number of people in a population.	4.
5. Fatal disease transmitted by contaminated water.	5.
6. Ceremony of crowning a monarch.	6.
7. Woman employed to teach and train children in a family.	7.
8. Freedom of a national minority or colony to govern itself under the overall control of the British government.	8.
9. Goes abroad to preach or carry out charitable work.	9.
10. Child who taught simple lessons to younger ones.	10.
11. Woman employed to look after children in a nursery.	11.
12. Bicycle with a big wheel in front and a small one behind.	12.
13. System passed by parliament to stop foreign goods being imported.	13.
14. Disguised as women, men in Wales organised these to protest against toll charges on roads.	14.
15. Area of crowded, squalid houses.	15.
16. Women who fought for the right to vote.	16.
17. Goods made from woollen cloth.	17.
18. Type of bus powered by electricity and running on rails.	18.
19. Sending criminals abroad as punishment.	19.
20. Injection with a dead or weakened form of a disease to protect against the virulent form.	20.

A VICTORIAN QUIZ

Try these questions

1. Who was Baroness Lehzen?

2. Who or what was Dizzy?

3. Who was known as the *Lady of the Lamp?*

4. Who or what was the *sick man of Europe* in the 19th. century?

5. What was an anti-maccassar?

6. Why were Dr. Barnardo's homes formed?

7. Who founded the Salvation Army?

8. (i) When was Victoria born? (ii) When did she ascend the throne?
(iii) When did she die? [Give exact dates.]

9. Give the population of London in 1851.

10. There was a cholera epidemic in 1832. How many people died approximately?

11. What tragedy in 1861 devastated Queen Victoria?

12. Give the exact date of the opening of the Great Exhibition.

13. In 1853, Russia invaded Turkish territory. Name the war that followed.

14. Where is the Crimea?

15. Who wrote the book, *The Origin of Species?*

16. In 1851, a census was taken of those who attended church. What was the result?

17. Name the leader of social reform in the 1830s.

18. What did the Ten Hour Act do for women and children?

19. *Until the 1840s, children did not have to go to school.* True or false?

20. What were 'ragged' schools?

21. Give the date of the first FA Cup Final.

22. Why did 2 million Irishmen emigrate to America between 1840 - 1860?

23. Name the leader of the Irish Home Rule movement in the late 1870s.

VICTORIAN TIME-LINE

Select the correct dates for each of the events below from this list.

1837, 1840, 1842, 1847, 1851, 1861, 1863, 1866, 1867, 1870, 1872, 1878, 1891, 1897, 1899, 1901.

DATE	EVENT
	The Ten Hours Act (children 13 - 18 years old not allowed to work more than 10 hours a day).
	Nearly 6,000 people died in London from cholera.
	Great Exhibition held in Crystal Palace, London.
	Suffragette Movement started.
	Prince Albert died.
	First electric trains in London.
	Mines Act (children under 10 not allowed to work in mines).
	Dr. Thomas Barnardo founded the East End Juvenile Mission.
	First underground train in London.
	Queen Victoria and Prince Albert married.
	First FA Cup Final.
	Elizabeth Garrett Anderson became first woman doctor.
	Queen Victoria died.
	Salvation Army founded.
	Victoria became Queen.
	Children had to attend school until they were 12.

Now write these events and dates in the correct chronological order to make a Victorian time-line. Add any other events and their dates that you think are important.

CLASS AND FAMILY LIFE

Below are typical households adapted from the Census of 1851. Use the information to answer the questions which follow.

1. Household Position/Occupation (Age)
Sir George Ponsonby - head, baronet (65)
Beatrice, Lady Ponsonby - wife (53)
Charlotte Ponsonby - granddaughter, scholar (18)
William Evans - butler, married (41)
Thomas Jones - coachman, married (50)
Susan Davies - cook , married (45)
Henry Davies - stable boy (15)
Mary Anne Roberts - lady's maid (34)
Sarah Pudsey - lady's maid (22)
Rebecca Thomas - housemaid (18)
Rita Gascoyne- housemaid 19)
Susan Rushworth - kitchen maid(18)

3. Household Position/Occupation (Age)
William Johns - head, chemist and druggist (42)
Jane Johns - wife (33)
William Johns - son (7)
Ellen Johns - daughter (2)
Frederick Entwhistle - apprentice (14)
Ann Summerfield - housemaid (23)
Rose Isaacs - nursemaid (16)

2. Household Position/Occupation (Age)
William Ashdown - head, solicitor (50)
Elizabeth Ashdown - wife (35)
Albert Ashdown - son (4)
Catherine Ashdown - daughter (3)
Mary Ashdown - daughter (2)
Olive Ashdown - daughter (3 months)
Sarah Entwhistle - cook, unmarried (32)
Betsey Bloggs - housemaid, unmarried (24)
Fanny Goodright - housemaid, unmarried (16)
Mary Birt - monthly nurse (67)

4. Household Position/Occupation (Age)
James Galsworthy - head, railway guard
Harriet Galsworthy - wife (22)
Walter Galsworthy - son (3)
James Galsworthy - son (2)
Eileen Galsworthy - daughter (3 months)
Emma Shibgo - nursemaid (12)

1. **To what class does Sir George Ponsonby belong? Give reasons for your answer?**
2. **From what class does William Ashdown come? How do you know?**
3. **To what classes do you think William Johns and James Galsworthy belong? Give reasons for your answer.**
4. **What do these statistics show about (a) the size of Victorian families and (b) the employment of servants?**
5. **These statistics suggest that the wife of the head of the household did not have employment outside the home. Suggest reasons for this. Compare with the situation today.**
6. **What would be possible occupations for the children from each of the families when they grow up?**
7. **Make a similar set of statistics for your family. How does it differ from the Victorian figures? Suggest reasons for the differences.**
8. **Write an account of a day in the life of Lady Ponsonby or Elizabeth Ashdown or Harriet Galsworthy.**

HOUSING CONDITIONS

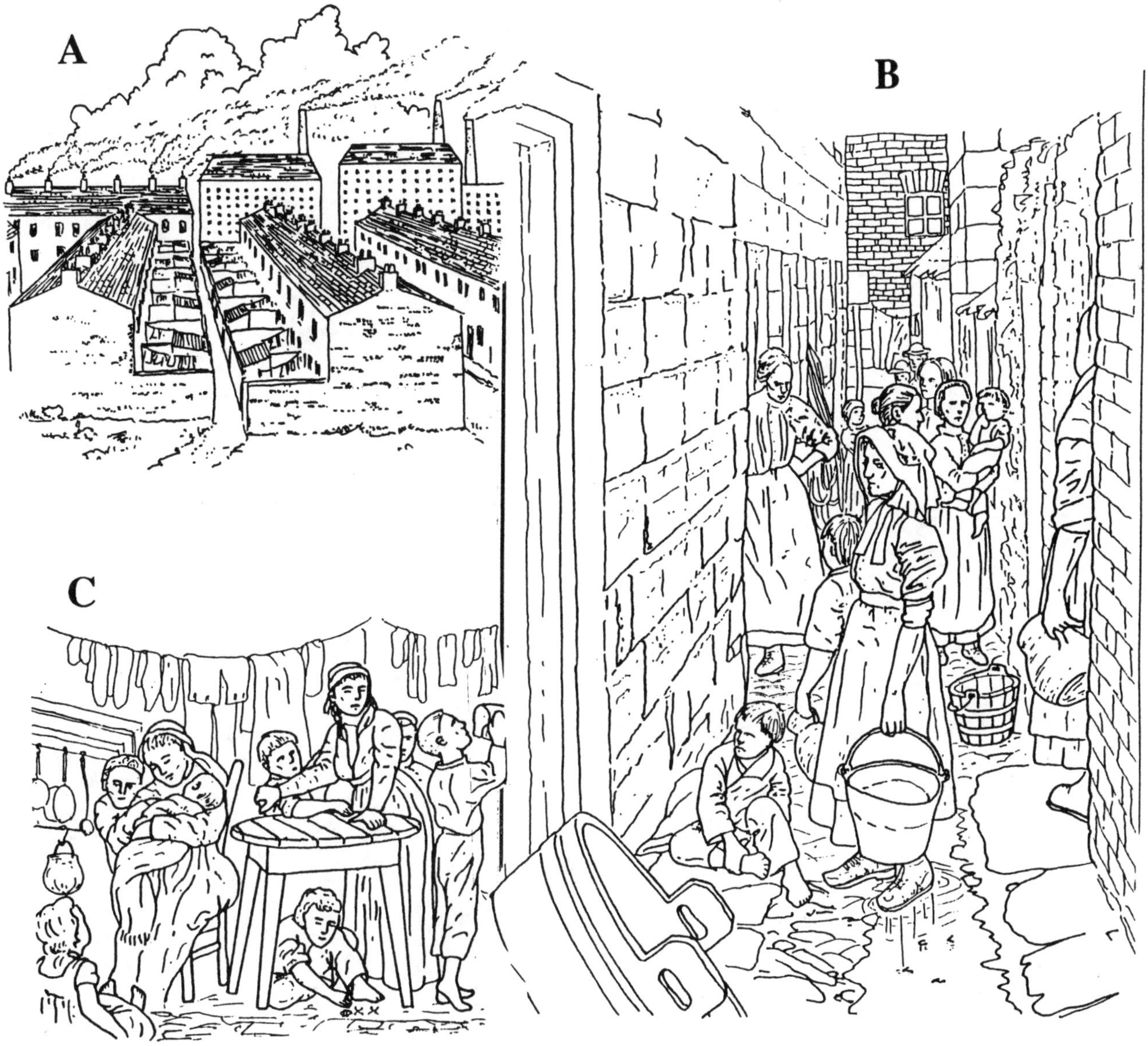

These drawings show how some people lived in Victorian times.

1. Who lived in these houses?
2. What kind of houses are they? Describe them.
3. Who built these houses and why?
4. What decided where these houses should be built?
5. There are several pails in the picture B. What were they used for and why were they needed?
6. Before, many of these people probably lived in the countryside. Why did they move to the towns?
7. 'There was no town planning and no sanitation.' What was the effect of this on living conditions and the health of the inhabitants of the new industrial towns?
8. How and where did wealthy industrialists live? Compare their houses and living conditions with those in the pictures.

HOUSING

The points below illustrate what it was like in a typical Victorian working class home. Read them and then answer the questions which follow.

a. Families lived in one room only.

b. Many people had to fetch their water from wells, pumps or streams.

c. Coal fires had to be lit to warm water.

d. There were no bathrooms or inside toilets. People usually washed from a bowl of water poured from a jug.

e. The houses were lit by candles or oil lamps.

f. There were no ready-made breakfast cereals.

g. There were no radios or televisions.

h. Most families were large with five or six children.

i. There was no public transport and there were no motor cars. Children had to walk to school.

j. There were newspapers but few people could read or afford them.

---

1. What obvious disadvantages were there when families lived (ate and slept) in one room?

2. *Water from wells, pumps or streams in Victorian times was often contaminated.* True or false.
***There were no reservoirs and no public water system.* What were the consequences of this?**

3. What replaced coal for heating as the 19th. century developed?

4. *People used horses for transport.* Give six disadvantages of this kind of transport.

5. What did people eat instead of ready-made breakfast cereals? What was the main diet of the working classes throughout the 19th. century?

6. Why were most people, especially the elderly, illiterate in the 19th. century? Why did this situation change in the 20th. century?

7. What forms of entertainment were available for the Victorian working classes?

8. Using the points (a) to (j) above, compare a Victorian home with yours.

9. Do you think life was harder for schoolchildren in Victorian times than it is today? Give reasons for your opinions.

10. Write a short essay on 'A Day in the Life of a Victorian Child from a Working Class Family.'

THE EMPLOYMENT OF CHILDREN

You have just been appointed to the position of a Government Inspector. Using the drawings below, write a report on the conditions in which children worked in Victorian times. Explain what the children are doing?

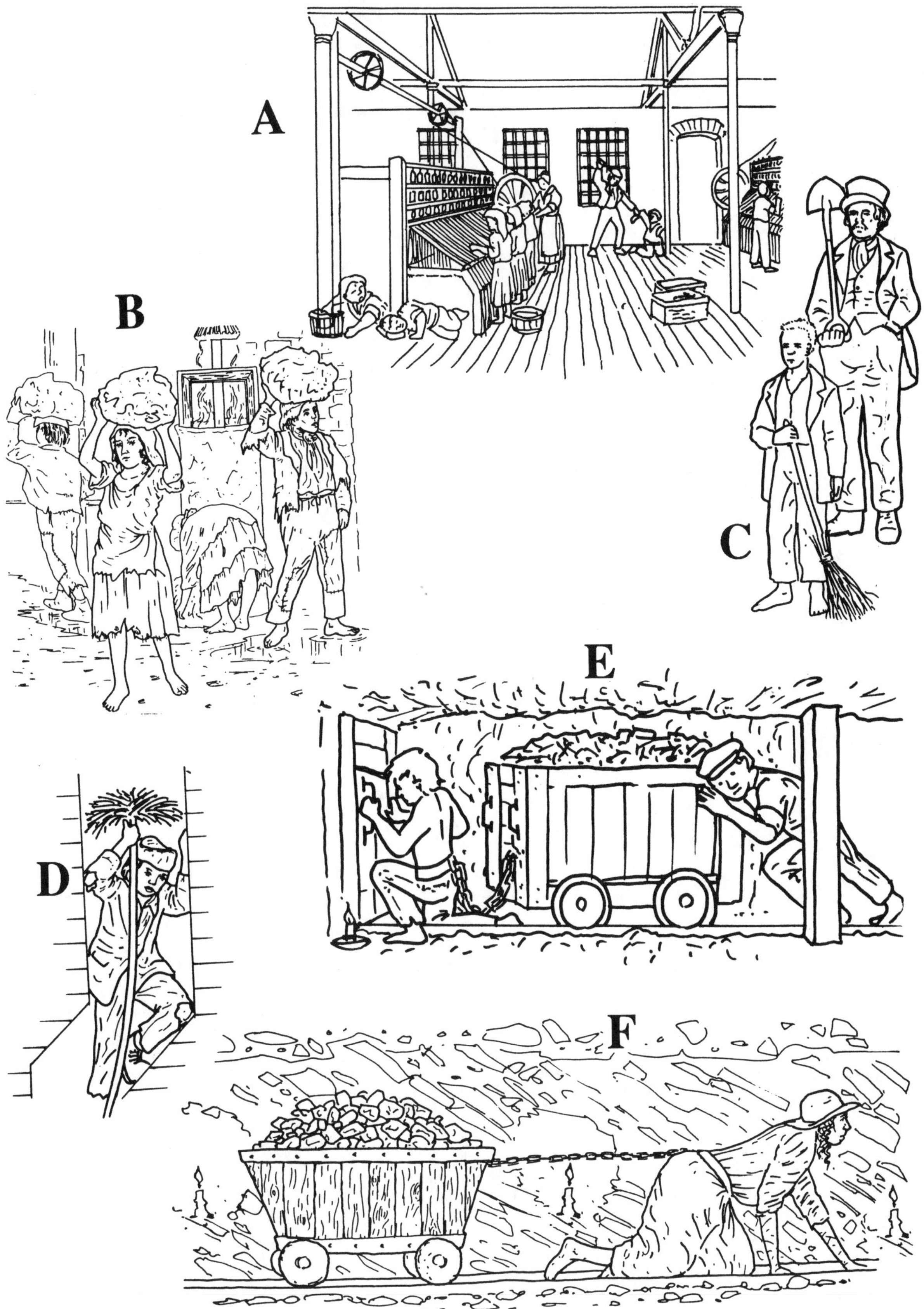

CHILDREN DOWN THE MINES

1. Read the following passages taken from reports of government inspectors on mines in the 19th. century. Then answer the questions which follow.

A He knows his place of work. It is inside one of the doors called trap-doors, which is in the barrow-way, for the purpose of forcing the stream of air which passes in its long many miled course from the down shaft to the up shaft of the pit; but which door must be opened whenever men or boys, with or without carriages, may wish to pass through. He seats himself in a little hole, about the size of a common fireplace, and with the string in his hand: and all his work is to pull that string when he has to open the door, and when man or boy has passed through, then to allow the door to shut of itself. Here it is his duty to sit, and be attentive, and pull his string promptly as anyone approaches. He may not stir above a dozen of steps with safety from his charge, lest he should be found neglecting his duty, and suffer for the same.

[Report on the work of an 8 year old boy, South Durham Mines, 1840.]

The next report concerns Catherine Thompson aged 11, deaf, she said, from a caning across the head in school when she was 6.

B I work with my sister who is 13. We start at six in the morning and return at six at night. We both work on father's account and draw his coal. The hutchies (carts) hold 8 cwt. which we have first to fill before we draw. The distance we draw is said to be a full 1,000 yards. I suffer much pains in my knee, which was crushed some time ago by a hutchie.

One of the doors was opened for Catherine by David Gay, aged 7 who said:

I gang (start) at half four in the morning and come up at half six at night. I can hardly get up the stairs-pit when work is done.

[Report on Redding collieries in Stirlingshire, 1840]

1. Describe the work the children are doing.

2. Give three reasons why the children were employed.

3. What do the passages tell you about (a) the type of work the children did and (b) the conditions in which they worked?

4. Explain 'be attentive' (line 7), 'pull his string promptly' (lines 7 - 8) ' and suffer for the same' (line 9), 'draw his coal' (line 12).

5. What do you understand by 'a hutchie' (line 14). How much coal did a hutchie hold?

6. Why was Catherine's knee so painful?

7. How many hours did David work?

8. How do you know David was very tired when his work was done?

9. What are used in modern mines instead of a 'stairs-pit' (line 16)?

10. Why are children not employed in mines today?

VICTORIAN ILLNESSES

This is a drawing of a doctor who has to visit four sick patients. Below each patient is a brief summary of their symptoms.

Patient A

This young girl is covered with spots all over her body. The spots leave scars on her face and abdomen. She has a very high temperature and the doctor fears she may go blind.

Patient B

This patient's face and neck are swollen. Her skin is turning black and she smells badly. She complains about being hot and has a very high temperature.

Patient C

complains of cramps and looks blue. He vomits all the time and spends most of his time on the toilet.

Patient D

complains that he is finding it difficult to breathe. He has lost weight and coughs often, sometimes spitting up blood.

1. **What do you think each patient is suffering from?**
   [Choose from cholera, consumption or tuberculosis, small pox, typhus.]
2. **What were the main treatments for such illnesses in the 19th. century?**
3. **Which of these diseases has been eradicated?**
4. **What was the main carrier of disease in the 19th. century?**
5. **Why did Victorians catch diseases so easily?**
6. **Victorians had large families. Explain why so many of the children died very young.**
7. **In Victorian times the medical profession was divided into three groups. Name them.**
8. **Give a brief account of the way in which Victorians lived which made them unhealthy.**
9. **Give an account of the way in which you live today which ensures that you keep healthy.**
10. **Write on the contributions of two people to the health of people in Victorian times. Choose two from Edward Jenner, James Simpson, Louis Pasteur and Joseph Lister.**

WOMEN'S RIGHTS

1. **What do you think was on the placards?**
2. **Why was the woman in chains?**
3. **Name the movement to which the woman belonged.**
4. **When did this movement develop? Name two important women who helped this movement.**
5. **What were the aims of this movement? Do you think they were important? Give reasons for your answer.**
6. **What was Queen Victoria's attitude to the emancipation of women?**
7. ***In early Victorian times, upper and middle class women stayed at home, only the husbands went out to work.* True or false?**
8. **Compare and contrast the position of women in Victorian society in (a) 1837 and (b) 1901.**
9. ***Women finally obtained democratic freedom in the early 20th. century but these rights were hardly worth fighting for and certainly not worth dying for.* Do you agree? Give reasons for your opinions.**
10. **Using the headings below, compare women's rights today with the rights of women in 1850. One comparison has been done for you.**

1850	Today
No rights over property.	Full rights over property.

EDUCATION

These objects could be found in a Victorian classroom. What are they and what were they used for? Which are still used today? Do you have any of these objects in your school?

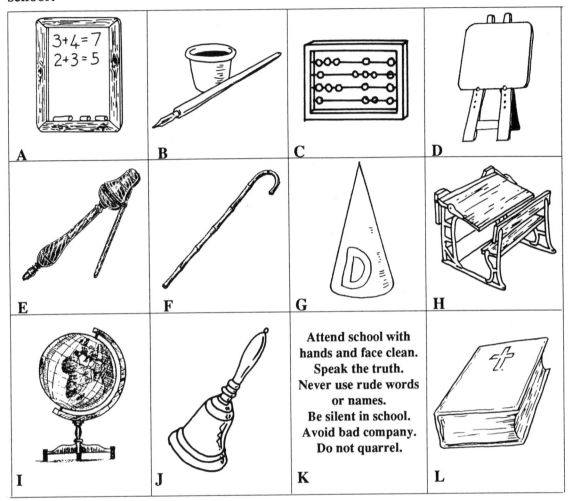

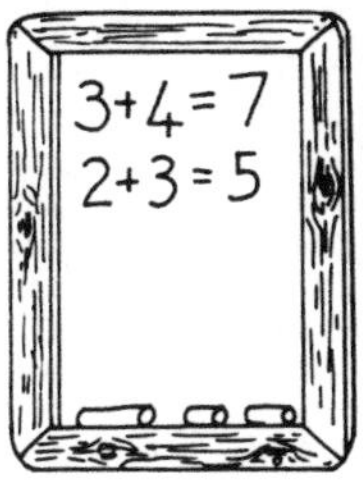 A	 B	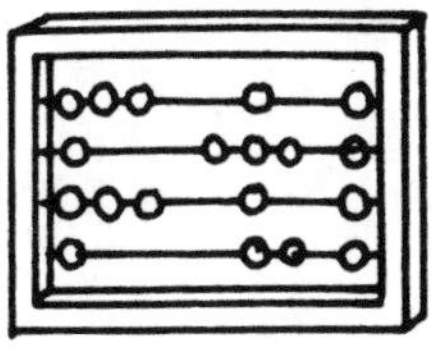 C	 D
 E	 F	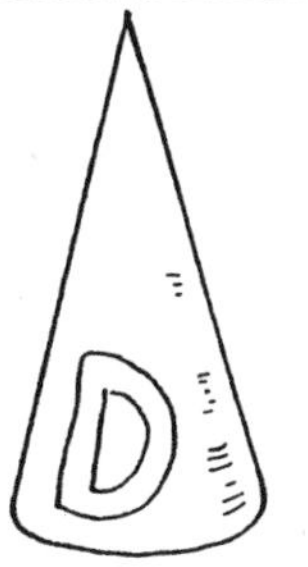 G	 H
 I	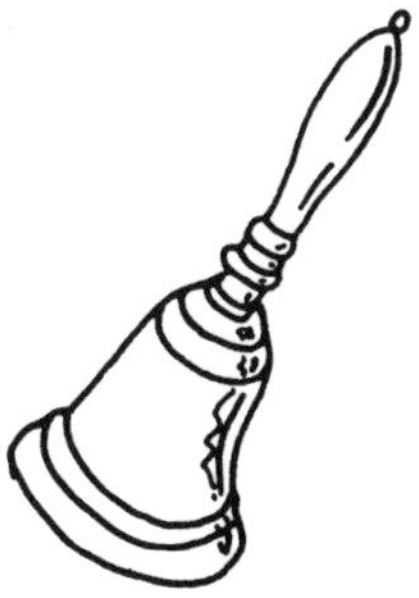 J	**Attend school with hands and face clean. Speak the truth. Never use rude words or names. Be silent in school. Avoid bad company. Do not quarrel.** K	 L

Do you think object K is useful today?

Use (√) to indicate whether the following statements about Victorian schools were true or false.

STATEMENT	TRUE	FALSE
1. There were fifty or more children in a classroom.		
2. The teacher used a microphone.		
3. Children wrote on paper with biro pens.		
4. Much of the teaching was done by older pupils called monitors.		
5. Discipline was strict.		
6. Punishments were often harsh.		
7. Boys and girls were taught together in a classroom.		
8. All the children learned to play musical instruments.		
9. Children were taught by repetition.		
10. Visual aids were displayed on classroom walls.		

CLASSROOMS

A

1. Which of these classrooms is Victorian?
2. Which classroom has the most equipment?
3. Make a list of the differences between the two classrooms.
4. What similarities are there?
5. What do these two pictures tell you about how the teaching of children has changed?
6. Which classroom would you prefer to be taught in? Give reasons for your answer.

B

EDUCATIONAL SOURCES

Below are two extracts taken from Victorian reports. Read them then answer the questions that follow.

A On some occasions, I have observed children, who, trembling under the anticipated stroke, have lost all sense of the lesson in which they were engaged, and with eyes wandering from their book to the avenging rod, have brought upon themselves, as they caught the master's eye, the blow. At other times, I have witnessed a master step into a class where was some little inattention or disturbance, and deal out boxes on the ear, blows on the head, and cuffs on the back, promiscuously on all within his reach, and then, as though he had done all that duty required him, return to his seat.

(Minutes of the Committee of Council on Education, 1844, Vol. II, p. 234.)

1. **What does this passage tell you about corporal punishment in the Victorian classroom?**
2. **What was the 'avenging rod'? Why did the children watch it?**
3. **Do you think the way in which discipline was kept helped the children to learn? Give reasons for your answer.**
4. **'... as though he had done all that duty required him ... ' What does this mean and what does it tell you about teaching at this time?**

B We blame masters, and we blame monitors, and we punish children: we find fault with methods and systems, and rooms and stiuations; but we often leave untouched the tap-root of all the evil - the parent... You find a group of children in the street playing at marbles, it may be, during school-hours. 'Why are you not at school today?' - 'Mother sent me for a bit of coal, Sir'; or 'Mother's gone out, and I stayed to watch baby'; or 'Mother said I wo'rnt to go this morning'; or 'Please, Sir, mother wanted me..' It really seems that there is no errand so short nor business so trifling as not, in the mother's eyes, to be more important than for her child to be late or to be absent from school.

(Minutes of the Committee of Council on Education, 1884, Vol. II, p. 274.)

1. **What is the 'evil' in passage B?**
2. **Who is usually blamed for this 'evil'?**
3. **What is meant by the 'tap-root' of the evil?**
4. **Who is thought to be really responsible for the problem discussed in the passage?**
5. **'... there is no errand so short nor business so trifling as not, in the mother's eyes, to be more important than for her child to be late or to be absent from school' What does this mean?**
6. **Does the problem discussed in this passage exist today? How do the circumstances differ today?**

TIMETABLES AND CURRICULUM

A VICTORIAN SCHOOL | **SCHOOL TODAY**

9 am	Assembly
9.30	Bible reading
10.00	Writing
10.30	Break
10.50	Arithmetic
11.30	Singing
12.00	Lunch
12.30	Drill
2.00	Drill
3.00	Dictation
3.30	Reading
4.00	Home

1. Consider the timetable for a Victorian school above. What do you understand by the 3Rs? These were regarded as very important in Victorian times. Are they important today? Give reasons for your answer.

2. Explain 'dictation' and 'drill'? Are these used today?

3. In Victorian times, classes were big and there were not enough teachers. How were these problems dealt with? Was the solution satisfactory? Give reasons for your answer.

4. In the right hand column write out the timetable for a typical day in your school. Describe how your work schedule differs from the Victorian one. Are any subjects the same?

5. Write a brief description of a lesson in a Victorian classroom. Explain what you consider to be the bad and the good things about it.

6. Working class children were taught the 'basics', (the 3Rs) in Victorian times. Do you think it is a good idea that all should be taught the same things, that is that there should be a national curriculum?

7. How were children of wealthy Victorians educated?

8. What were the aims of early educationalists such as Hannah Moore? What are the aims of educationalists today?

9. Why were some members of the government of the day reluctant to educate the working class in Victorian times? From a political point of view, what are the advantages and disadvantages of a broad educational system for all?

10. Discuss the differences between the National Curriculum in Victorian times and today.

WRITING

Read the following passage and then answer the questions.

Victorian pupils learned the 3Rs - reading, writing and arithmetic. Writing was regarded as most important. When they started school (at about 5 years old) they were taught to write. First, they were taught to form the letters of the alphabet in a sand tray. Secondly, when they were older (from about 6 - 7) each child was given a slate and a slate pencil, a mug of water, a sponge and a stick with a mop on the end to wipe the slate clean. They practised for hours on end forming letters on these slates and wiping them off.

At the age of 8, they were given copybooks, pens and ink. The ink was made by mixing powder and water. The pens were made of wood with metal nibs and were dipped into the ink in inkwells. The nibs often made a scratchy noise as the children wrote. It was difficult to control the watery ink and the pens often made blots on the paper. The style of writing they practised in their copybooks was called 'copperplate'. This was like the writing engravers used on copperplated objects. The children usually copied simple sentences from the blackboard - facts about the days and months of the year, the seasons or scripture, history or geography. As they wrote, the teacher shouted at them and punished them if they blotted their copybooks.

1. **What do you understand by the three Rs and which one is considered in the passage?**
2. **What is the passage about? Suggest a title for it.**
3. **According to the passage, what were the stages in the Victorian methods used to teach children to write (a) at 5 years old, (b) at ages 6 - 7 and (c) at 8?**
4. **What did the children use to write on the slates?**
5. **How was the slate cleaned?**
6. **Why was a slate used?**
7. **How was ink made? What was it kept in?**
8. **Why was the ink difficult to use?**
9. **The style of writing the Victorian children practised was called copperplate. Why was it called this?**
10. **What kinds of things did the children usually write?**
11. **What did the teacher do as the children wrote in their copybooks?**
12. **What does 'blotted their copybooks' mean in the passage?**
13. **Why were teachers so keen to ensure children's copybooks were neat and tidy especially after 1862?**
14. **What does 'blot your copybook' mean today?**
15. **Do you think handwriting was more or less important in Victorian times than it is today? Give reasons for your answer.**

WRITING

VICTORIAN EATING HABITS

Read these two passages and then answer the questions which follow them.

A At twelve by the sun the teams would knock off for the dinner hour. Horses were unyoked and given their nosebags and men and boys threw themselves down on sacks spread out beside them and tin bottles of cold tea were uncorked and red handkerchiefs of food unwrapped. The lucky ones had bread and cold bacon, perhaps the top or the bottom of a cottage loaf, on which the small cube of bacon was placed. The less fortunate ones munched their bread and lard or morsel of cheese; and the boys with their ends of cold pudding were jokingly bidden not to get that 'ere treacle in their ears.'

From 'Larkrise' by Flora Thompson

B The dinner table was crowded ... In the centre stood a magnificent, finely spun, barley-sugar windmill, two feet and a half high, with a spacious sugar foundation ... The whole dinner, first, second, third, fourth course - everything, in fact, except dessert, was on the table ... Before Mr and Mrs Jorrocks were two great tureens of mock turtle soup, each capable of holding a gallon, and both full up to the brim. Then there were two sorts of fish: turbot and lobster sauce, and a great salmon. A round of boiled beef, and an immense piece of roast occupied the rear of these, ready to march on the disappearance of the fish and soup - and behind the walls, formed by the beef of old England, came two dishes of grouse, each dish holding three braces, the side dishes consisted of a calf's head hashed, a leg of mutton, chickens, ducks and mountains of vegetables; and round the windmill were plum pudding, tarts, jellies, pies and puffs.

From "Jorrock's Jaunts and Jollities" by R. S. Surtees

1. **These are descriptions of two main meals in the Victorian period. One is for labourers and the other for gentry. Which is which?**

2. **What are the main differences between these two meals?**

3. **Do you consider the two meals to be part of a balanced diet? Comment on the food eaten from this point of view.**

4. **What do these passages tell you about the way the two groups of diners lived?**

5. **Explain the following words and phrases from the passages:**
'knock off' **(line 1),** 'unyoked' **(line 2),** 'nosebags' **(line 2)** 'munched' **(line 6),** 'morsel' **(line 7),** 'bidden' **(line 8),** 'dessert' **(line 12),** 'up to the brim' **(line 14),** 'immense' **(line 15),** 'ready to march on the disappearance of the fish and soup' **(lines 16 - 17).**

6. **Write a menu for a main meal which you would enjoy and which would also be a healthy, balanced meal.**

VICTORIAN CLOTHES

Consider the advertisement above which appeared in *The Illustrated London News* at the end of the 19th. century. It shows a group beside the sea on a blowy Sunday morning. Answer the questions on Victorian dress using the drawing to help you.

1. **Describe in your own words the clothes worn by the people in the advertisement.**
2. **The young woman's waist is very small (it measures about 22 inches). How was this narrow waist achieved?**
3. **What are both women wearing over their skirts at the back just below the waistline?**
4. **What is this style of dress worn by the women called?**
5. **Name five things that both men are wearing /carrying.**
6. **What is the gentleman in the foreground wearing on his right eye?**
7. **What are the men wearing around their necks?**
8. **The clothes worn by the little girl are similar to those of the adult with her. What does this tell you about the way children were dressed in Victorian times?**
9. **Do you think people in this advertisement are (a) working class, (b) middle or upper class? Give reasons for your answer.**
10. **Draw this picture substituting suitable present-day clothes for the Victorian ones.**

POSTAL REFORM

A

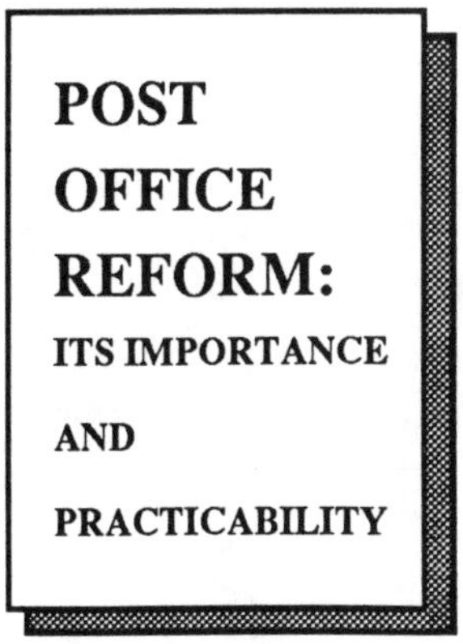

B

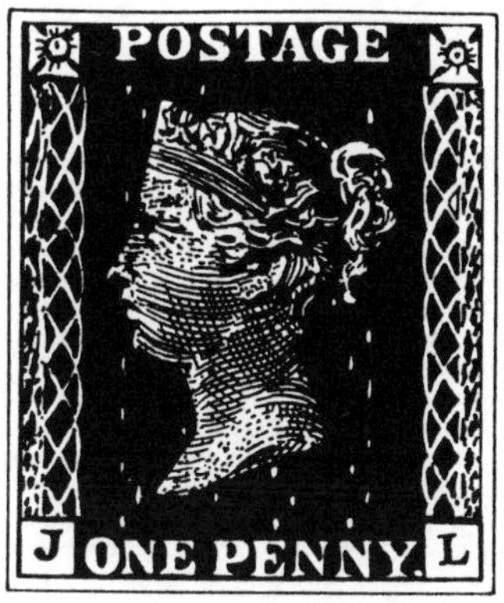

C

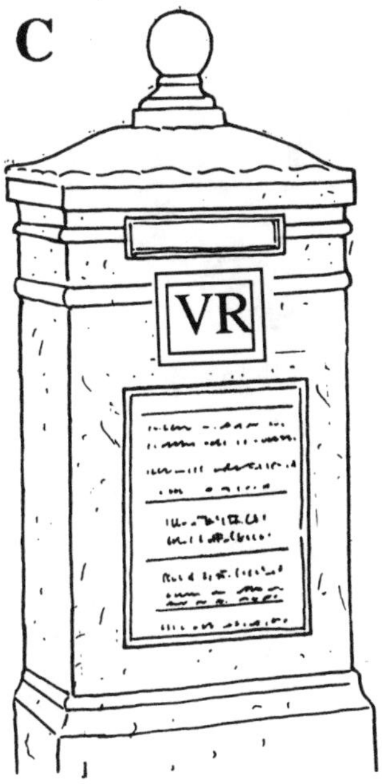

1. **Name the person who published this pamphlet (A) in 1838. Why was it so important?**

2. **Name the famous stamp (B). How did it get its name?**

3. **Today (B) is very valuable. True or false?**

4. **Why is there no country of origin shown on British stamps?**

5. **Suggest reasons why the development of a postal service was very important in Britain.**

6. **Expain why between 1839 - 1840 the profits of the post office fell by two-thirds although the volume of correspondence carried by the post office increased greatly.**

7. **When did pillar boxes first appear in London?**

8. **In the 1850s, the sender of a letter paid postage and it was customary for the recipient of the letter to pay the postman a halfpenny. When did this last charge stop?**

9. **What do the letters VR on the post office box in the drawing mean?**

10. **How much did it cost (approximately) to send a letter by post (a) before 1840, (b) after 1840?**

CRIME AND PUNISHMENT

1. These two drawings (A and B) show punishments inflicted on prisoners in Victorian times. Say what they are and write a short paragraph on each.

A

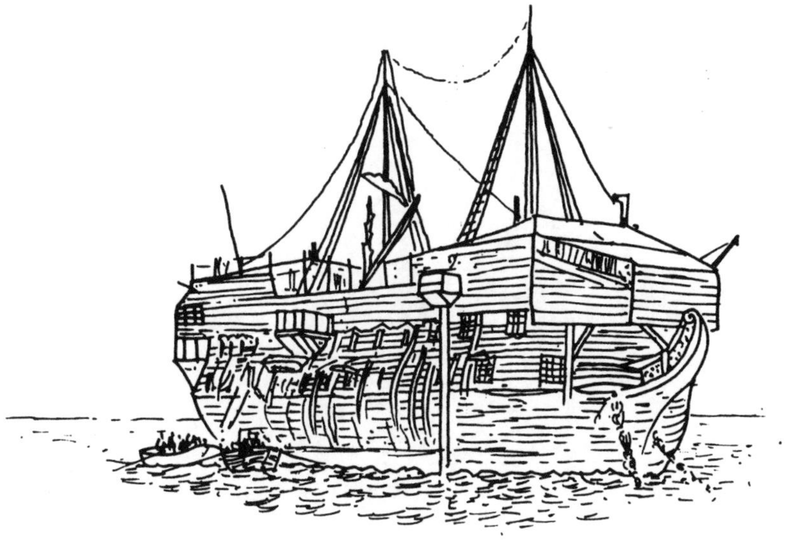

B

2. Complete the following by choosing the correct words from the list provided at the end of the passage.

In Victorian times, there was a great deal of poverty and much ..... as a result. In the big cities like London, there were a great many .... who made their living from mingling with and stealing from crowds in the streets. Some men organised bands of young .... to pick the pockets of the wealthy. Criminals were not often ...... because there was no organised ...... force until Sir Robert Peel founded his .... By 1839, there were police ...... all over the country. Criminals were dealt with .... Many men and women were .... or sent to .... Some were sent abroad to Botany Bay in .... Many died in .... ships on the way. The ships were moored on isolated river banks or near unhealthy swamps and .... Prisoners were ill-treated: they were seldom ... and lived in overcrowded conditions in .... because they were not allowed to talk to each other.

[Australia, caught, children, convict, crime, fed, flogged, forces, harshly, marshes, pickpockets, peelers, police, prison, silence.]

THE WORKHOUSE

Look at the drawings below carefully, then answer the questions which follow.

A

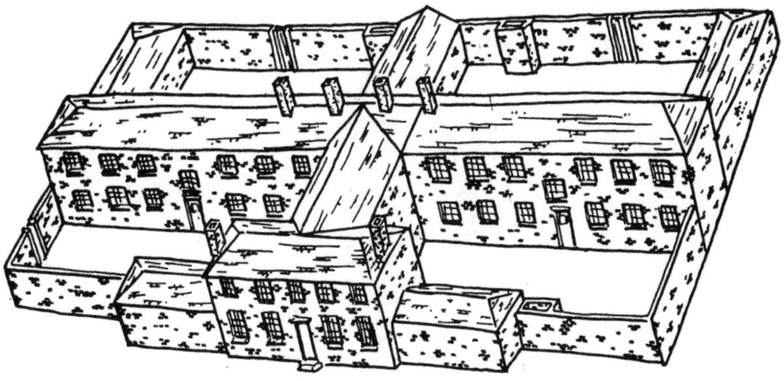

B

A This is a drawing of the outside of a Victorian workouse.

1. **What was a workhouse and why were people sent there?**
2. **Write briefly about life in a workhouse. Discuss the things which you consider to be cruel.**
3. **What were the aims of the workhouse system? How successful was it?**

B This is a drawing of a well known scene from *Oliver Twist* by Charles Dickens.

1. **Where is Oliver?**
2. **What is Oliver asking for?**
3. **What do you think was the reaction to Oliver's request? (Look at the expression on the woman's face.)**
4. **What does the appearance of Oliver tell you about him?**
5. **Write an account of this scene in your own words.**
6. **Ask your teacher or a parent to read *Oliver Twist* to you especially this part of the story.**

VICTORIAN LITERATURE

Read the passages below then answer the questions which follow them.

A

'Hold your noise!" cried a terrible voice, as a man started up from among the graves at the side of the church porch. 'Keep still, you little devil, or I'll cut your throat!'

A fearful man, all in coarse grey, with a great iron on his leg. A man with no hat, and with broken shoes, and with an old rag tied round his head. A man who had been soaked in water, and smothered in mud, and lamed by stones, and cut by flints, and stung by nettles, and torn by briars; who limped and shivered, and glared and growled; and whose teeth chattered in his head as he seized me by the chin.

'O! Don't cut my throat, sir,' I pleaded in terror. 'Pray don't do it, sir.'

'Tell us your name!' said the man. 'Quick!'

'Pip, Sir.'

'Once more,' said the man, staring at me. 'Give it mouth!'

'Pip. Pip, sir.'

From *Great Expectations* by Charles Dickens

1. **What do you think the man who approached Pip is?**
2. **Describe how the man in the church yard is dressed. Why did he have 'a great iron on his leg'? Explain this.**
3. **Why was Pip so afraid?**
4. **Explain the meaning of 'Give it mouth!'**
5. **What does Dickens tell us about the nature and circumstances of the man by the words 'A man with no hat ... glared and growled;'? [Lines 3 - 6]**

B

Once upon a time there was a little chimney-sweep and his name was Tom. He lived in a great town in the North country, where there were plenty of chimneys to sweep. He could not read nor write ... and he never washed himself, for there was no water ... where he lived ... He cried when he had to climb the dark flues, rubbing his poor knees and elbows raw; and when the soot got into his eyes ... and when he was tossing half-pennies with the other boys, or playing leap-frog ... As for chimney-sweeping, and being hungry, and being beaten he stood manfully with his back to it till it was over, as the old donkey did to a hailstorm.

From *The Water Babies* by Charles Kingsley in 1863.

1. **Do you think Tom was young or old? Was he big or small? Give reasons for your answers.**
2. **Why could Tom neither read nor write? [Lines 2 - 3].**
3. **Why was there no water? [Line 3].**
4. **Give the meaning of 'dark flues' [line 4] and 'elbows raw' [line 4].**
5. **How do we know from the passage that Tom was ill-treated?**
6. **What did Tom do in his spare time?**
7. **What do the words 'as the old donkey did to a hailstorm' [line 7] tell us about Tom and about what his master thought of him?**
8. **What does the passage tell us about children in Victorian times?**
9. **How and why had the kind of situation described in the passage changed by 1900?**

VICTORIAN ARITHMETIC

Today, goods cost about 45 times as much as they did in Victorian times. This means that something costing £1 then would cost £45 now or something costing 2p in Victorian times would cost 90p now.

1. Compare the cost of food in Victorian times and now by completing this table.

Average cost in Victorian times	Cost today
potatoes $\frac{1}{2}$ p lb	
bread 1p loaf	
cheese 4p lb	
butter 5p lb	
bacon 5p lb	
eggs 4p for 12	
sugar 3p lb	
milk 1p pint	
meat 3p lb	
tea 20p lb	

[Remember that 1 lb is approximately 450 g and 1$\frac{3}{4}$ pints is approximately 1 litre.]

2. Which item in this Victorian price list was very expensive but is now a common and important part of the British diet?

3a. Make a list of what you think a working class family of 8 (mother, father and six children) would need for one week. How much would this have cost? The father would have earned about £2 a week. What percentage of his wages would have been spent on food?

3b. How does the wage bill compare with the cost of a similar food list today? What other food items would you expect the family to buy today?

4. A manual worker earned about £2 a week in Victorian times. Allowing for the changes in the value of money, how does this compare with the wages earned today?

5. HAXELL'S ROYAL EXETER HOTEL, West Strand. Newly decorated, refurnished. Apartment and most liberal board 10s. 6d daily, bedrooms 2s. 6d.

Advertisement in *The Times,* Friday , June 2 1876.

How much would it have cost to stay in this hotel for a week (i) full board, (ii) room only? Give your answers in 'Victorian money'. What would it have cost today?

6. TEETH 132 Oxford-street. MR BARCLAY'S SPECIALITIES: all cases guaranteed, failure impossible: springs, wires or bands of every description avoided; no pain or extractions required. Consultations from 22s.6d.

Comment on this advertisement from *The Times.,* June 2 1876.

[In Victorian times £1 = 240d 12d = 1s 20s = £1 Also 2s.6d or 2/6 = 12$\frac{1}{2}$p]

[Today £1 = 100p]

VICTORIAN ARITHMETIC

WAGES AND EMPLOYMENT

1. Table A shows the number of indoor domestic servants and table B shows the annual wages for female domestic servants in London in 1895.

A

Date	Number of indoor domestic servants
1851	751,541
1861	962,786
1871	1,204,477
1881	1,230,406
1891	1,386,167
1901	1,285,072
1911	1,271,990

B

Age	Servants in upper and middle class class families	Girls from workhouse
13	-	£5.16s.
15	£7.2s	£6.16s.
17	£9.18s	£9.0s.
20	£15.0s	£11.10s
21 - 25	£17.8s.	£12.4s.
26 - 30	£19.18s.	£12.18s.
40+	£24.12s	-

[20s = £1. Also £1 in Victorian times is worth about £45 now]

From Table A

1. The number of domestic servants was at its lowest in 18 . . . . . and at its highest in 18 . . . .

2. Why do you think the number of servants began to fall at the beginning of the century?

From Table B

3. How much did a 15 year old servant in an upper class family earn in a week?

4. How much did a 15 year old servant from the workhouse earn in a week?

5. Why do you think wages rose with age?

6. How do these wages compare with today's earnings?

7. What was the top wage for a servant?

8. Why do you think the wages of girls from the workhouse were lower than the others?

2. Read this extract from a letter Mrs. Ruby Ponsonby wrote to her friend about a new kitchen maid, Alice, who earns £5.16s a year and is 13 years old. Then answer the questions which follow.

Dear Anne ... Two months ago we engaged a new girl called Alice to help in the kitchen. She is finding the work very difficult and giving Cook no end of trouble. Cook told her to black the kitchen stove but the silly girl got blacking all over her and ruined her new apron. After giving her a good slapping, Cook put her in a hot bath and scrubbed her down. I fined her one shilling for being so stupid but I think she will improve if we persevere. Indeed, if she works well, I might give her an afternoon off soon to visit her family. Yesterday, I gave her a prayerbook which she treasures. Edward says I am too soft hearted with the staff, especially the pretty ones. ...

Your affectionate friend, Ruby.

1. Would this 13 year old have been working if she lived in Britain today? Give reasons for your answer.

2. What is meant by 'to black the kitchen stove'.

3. Comment on the treatment the girl received for getting the blacking all over herself and her new apron. Do you think the treatment was justified?

4. Do you think the kitchen maid was overpaid or underpaid?

5. What can you learn about holiday obligations from the passage?

A VICTORIAN GAME

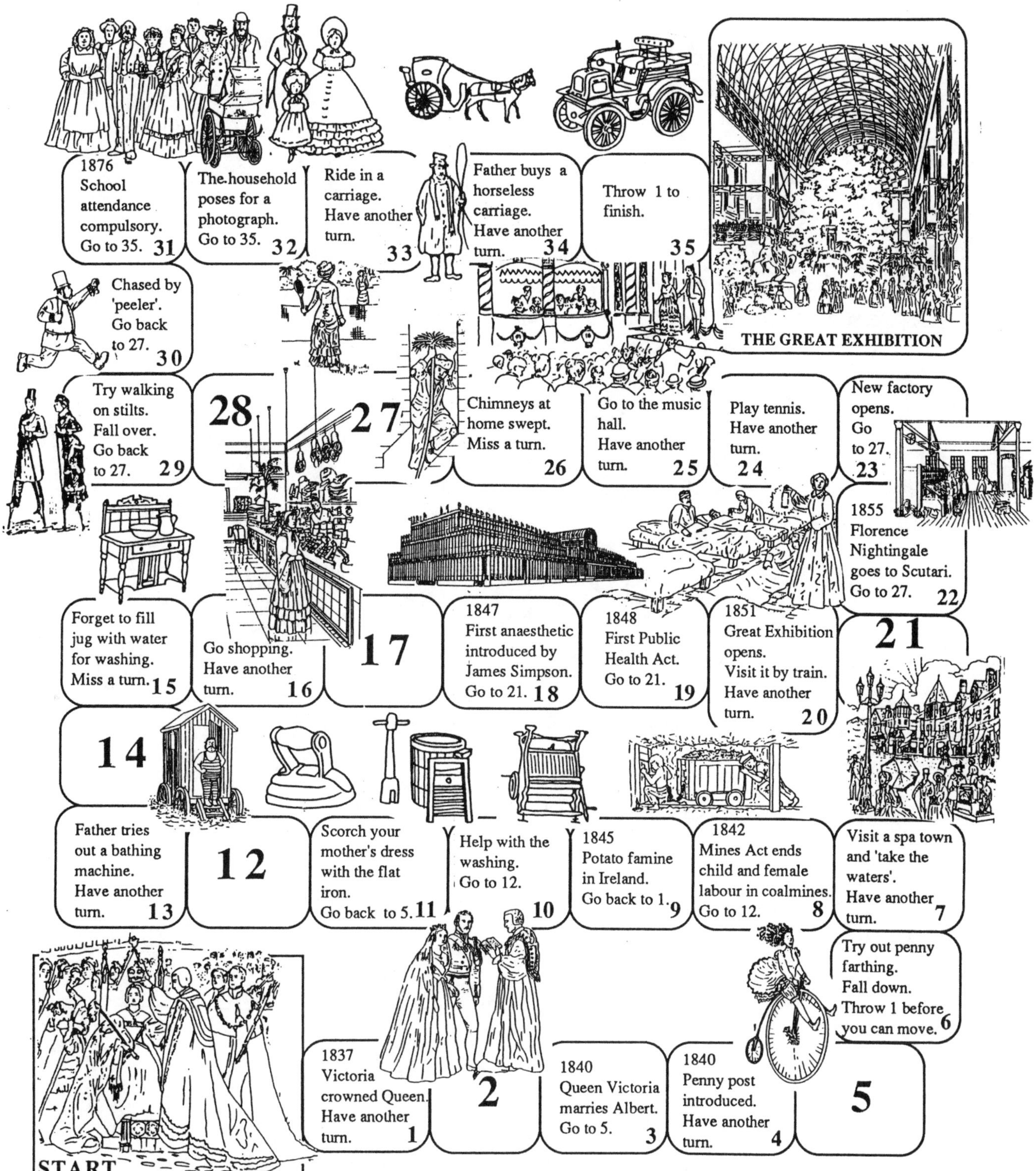
START
1837 Victoria crowned Queen. Have another turn. 1
2
1840 Queen Victoria marries Albert. Go to 5. 3
1840 Penny post introduced. Have another turn. 4
5
Try out penny farthing. Fall down. Throw 1 before you can move. 6
Visit a spa town and 'take the waters'. Have another turn. 7
1842 Mines Act ends child and female labour in coalmines. Go to 12. 8
1845 Potato famine in Ireland. Go back to 1. 9
Help with the washing. Go to 12. 10
Scorch your mother's dress with the flat iron. Go back to 5. 11
12
Father tries out a bathing machine. Have another turn. 13
14
Forget to fill jug with water for washing. Miss a turn. 15
Go shopping. Have another turn. 16
17
1847 First anaesthetic introduced by James Simpson. Go to 21. 18
1848 First Public Health Act. Go to 21. 19
1851 Great Exhibition opens. Visit it by train. Have another turn. 20
21
1855 Florence Nightingale goes to Scutari. Go to 27. 22
New factory opens. Go to 27. 23
Play tennis. Have another turn. 24
Go to the music hall. Have another turn. 25
Chimneys at home swept. Miss a turn. 26
27
28
Try walking on stilts. Fall over. Go back to 27. 29
Chased by 'peeler'. Go back to 27. 30
1876 School attendance compulsory. Go to 35. 31
The household poses for a photograph. Go to 35. 32
Ride in a carriage. Have another turn. 33
Father buys a horseless carriage. Have another turn. 34
Throw 1 to finish. 35
THE GREAT EXHIBITION

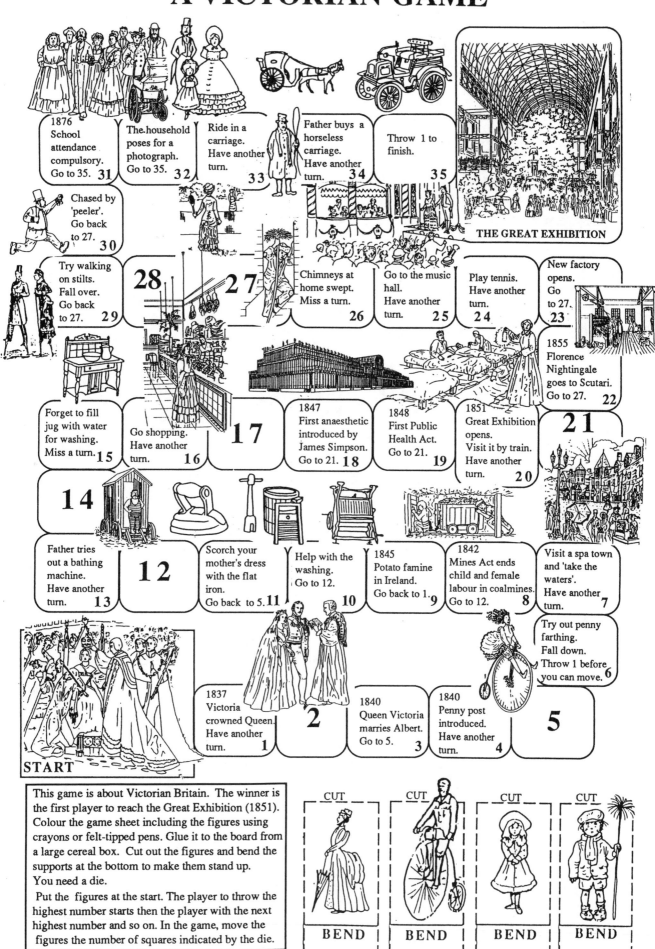

This game is about Victorian Britain. The winner is the first player to reach the Great Exhibition (1851). Colour the game sheet including the figures using crayons or felt-tipped pens. Glue it to the board from a large cereal box. Cut out the figures and bend the supports at the bottom to make them stand up.
You need a die.

Put the figures at the start. The player to throw the highest number starts then the player with the next highest number and so on. In the game, move the figures the number of squares indicated by the die.

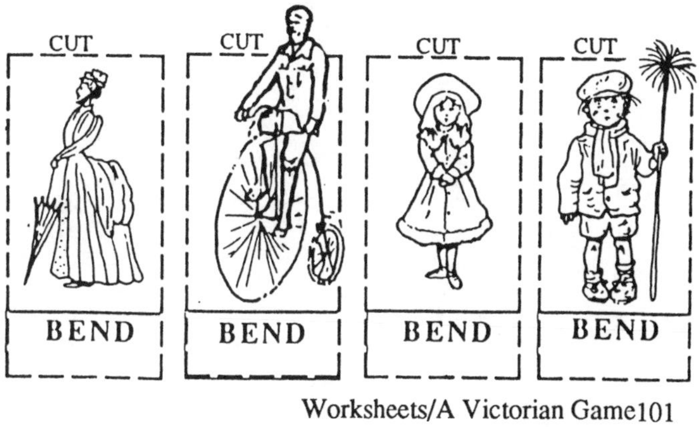
CUT
CUT
CUT
CUT
BEND
BEND
BEND
BEND

PROJECT IDEAS

1. Life in Victorian times.
2. A Victorian family.
3. Victorian children.
4. Women in Victorian times.
5. The Man in Victorian society.
6. Food and diet in Victorian times.
7. Victorian roads.
8. The position of the horse in Victorian society.
9. Train Mania.
10 Science and medicine in the 19th. century.
11. A famous politician.
12. A famous scientist.
13. A road builder.
14. A famous engineer.
15. A famous schoolmaster.
16. The suffragettes.
17. Isambard Kingdom Brunel.
18. The life and work of Charles Dickens.
19. Famous steam locomotives.
20. Famous steamships.
21. The workhouse in Victorian times.
22. The poor in Victorian times.
23. The middle class in Victorian times.
24. The rich in Victorian times.
25. The Queen's Consort.
26. Royal children.
27. Osborne, Isle of Wight.
28. Historical sources - the Victorians.
29. Photography in the 19th. century.
30. Famous Victorians.
31. The life and work of Florence Nightingale.
32. Famous Victorian leaders.
33. The coming of the 'horseless carriage'.
34. Gas and electricity.
35. The beginnings of the post office.
36. Victorian explorers.
37. Victorian missionaries.
38. Victorian soldiers.
39. Famous Victorian buildings.
40. The Great Exhibtion, 1851.
41. William Morris and his art.
42. The Pre-Raphaelite Movement.
43. The Irish Problem.
44. The Eastern Question.
45. War in the Crimea.
46. Law and order.
47. Crime and punishment.
48. The Victorian Age through the eyes of Charles Dickens.
49. Public health problems - 19th. century style.
50. 'Britain - the Workshop of the World.'

THINGS TO MAKE

1. A Victorian bookmark.
2. A Victorian brooch.
3. A Victorian greetings card.
4. A Victorian Christmas card.
5. A Victorian sampler.
6. A Victorian patchwork.
7. A desk tidy decorated with Victorian illustrations.
8. A tidy box decorated with Victorian illustrations.
9. Puppets of Victorian characters for a play.
10. A magic lantern.
11. A kaleidoscope.
12. A Victorian flick book.
13. A Victorian paperweight. (Paint a Victorian character on a smooth pebble or shell.)
14. A Victorian address book.
15. A Victorian diary.
16. A Victorian newspaper rack.
17. A Victorian Dundee cake.
18. A Victorian Punch or Judy.
19. Victorian ginger wine.
20. A Victorian hat.
21. A Victorian snuffbox.
22. A Victorian notebook.
23. A Victorian dunces cap.
24. A Victorian hoop.
25. A Victorian cartoon.
26. A Victorian stamp or photograph album.
27. A Victorian pressed flower book.
28. A Victorian recipe book.
29. A Victorian Christmas cracker.
30. An embroidered Victorian handkerchief.

ANSWERS

Of course, there may be several alternative, or additional acceptable answers to some of the questions.

Page 63

1. 20th., June, 1837. 2. 18 years old.
3. William IV.
4. The Archbishop of Canterbury and Lord Conyngham, the Lord Chamberlain. 5. Dutiful.

Page 64

1. King George III reigned 1760 - 1820.
King George IV reigned 1820 - 1830.
King William IV reigned 1830 - 1837.
Queen Victoria married Prince Albert, Duke of Saxony, Prince of Saxe-Coburg and Gotha on 10th. February 1840.
Queen Victoria reigned 1837 - 1901.
King Edward VII reigned 1901 - 1910.

2.

1819 Birth of Queen Victoria
1837 Victoria crowned Queen.
1840 Queen Victoria married her cousin, Prince Albert.
1861 Death of the Prince Consort Albert from typhoid.
1876 Queen Victoria became Empress of India.
1887 The Queen's Golden Jubilee.
1897 Queen Victoria's Diamond Jubilee.
1901 Death of Queen Victoria.

3. 'Drina.' 4. The 'Widow of Windsor.'
5. 64 years.

Page 66

1. Gramophone, 2. child's doll,
3. slate and slate pencils, 4. abacus (used for counting),
5. lady's fan, 6. chimney sweep's brushes,
7. pen and inkwell, 8. bathing machine,
9. a canal barge, 10. dunce's cap and canes used for punishment.

Page 67

1. Primary. See Teachers' Notes.
2. The Crimean War. Britain and France supported Turkey against Russia.
3. At Scutari Hospital in southern Russia. She had cared for sick and wounded British soldiers.
4. 'as the lady with the lamp.'
5. 'Entertain' - have; 'devotion' - dedication; 'admiration' - respect; 'alleviating' - lessening.
6. A brooch. It was appropriate because it was unsolicited and showed how much the Queen valued the contribution of Florence Nightingale to the war effort. The nurse was regarded as an angel of mercy.
7. Mary Seacole.
8. Nursing which now became a respectable profession for women.
9. The Nightingale Training School for Nurses.
10. It was a step in the emancipation of women.

Page 68

Disraeli and India

1. He had bought shares in the Suez Canal for Britain. 1876. The Khedive Ishmael.
2. The Sphinx. Egypt.
3. See Teachers' Notes.
4. It shortened the distance travelled by ship between Great Britain, India and the Far East.
5. The Right Move? (for example).

Page 68 (cont).

The Crimean War

1. The Charge of the Light Brigade, 1854.
2. See Teachers' Notes. The attack was badly organised.
3. The charge was a disaster and 'A Trump Card' would usually suggest success. 'Card' is also a pun on the name of Lord Cardigan who was responsible for the engagement. He was blamed for its disastrous consequences.
4. 'The Valley of Death', The Disasters of War', 'A Shameful Defeat' ...
5. They had little or no ability with respect to leading men in war and they needed more training for battle situations.

Page 69

1. 24th. April, 1869.
2. Five pence (less than half a penny now).
Some other pages or a smaller magazine called a supplement.
3. Printed in black and white.
Lithographed not photographed.
The way people are dressed in the cover illustration.
Most men are wearing top hats and the women are wearing bonnets.
No motorised vehicles present.
Boats on the Thames are mostly rowing and sailing boats.
There are also a number of steam vessels.
No cranes in front of the wharves.
The style of the decorative print of the title, 'Illustrated London News'.
4. Original.
5. List them on a register at the Post Office so they could be sent by mail.
6. The River Thames. 7. Oarsmen.
8. Few illustrations, few pictures, black and white (no colour), smaller print than today.

Page 70

The Rainhill Trials

2. The directors of the new railway line being constructted (the Liverpool and Manchester Railway) ran a competition fo find the best steam engine which met certain specified conditions which they laid down in a prospectus. The owner of the best steam engine would win a prize of £500.

Those taking part were:
Timothy Burstall and his engines 'Perseverance' and 'Cycloped';
Timothy Hackworth and his engine 'Sans Pareil';
John Braithwaite and John Erricson and their engine 'Novelty';
George and Robert Stephenson and their engine 'Rocket'.
The winners were the Stephensons.

Queen Victoria's Train

1. Carriages had improved, become more sophisticated and were suitable for passengers.
2. The boom in building new railways throughout Britain. (1836 - 37 and 1844 - 47)
3. Labourers who helped to construct the railways - laying track, building viaducts and tunnels.
4. The Liverpool and Manchester Line opened by the Duke of Wellington on 15th. September, 1839.

Page 71

1. Between 1830 and 1844 with a peak between 1842 - 44. They were protesting against paying tolls to use the roads. Toll gates had been erected to stop people using them unless they paid.
2. In South Wales. Yes, there was a serious riot in Bedminster almost a century earlier (1749).
3. They attacked at night, suddenly and without warning. They destroyed the gates and tollhouses but did not harm the tollkeepers.
4. Male, men dressed as women. They took their motto from the words in Genesis 24:60, 'And they blessed Rebekah and said to her ... may your descendants possess the gate of those who hate them.'
5. A tollhouse where the tollkeeper lived.
6. There was social dissatisfaction because of changes in agriculture, increased tithe charges and the changes brought about by the Poor Law Amendment Act of 1834.
7. The government sent soldiers and police to South Wales and the disorders ceased.
8. Lord Cawdor's Act in this year amended the turnpike trust laws in South Wales and lessened the burden of the tollgate system.

Page 72

1. A motor car. 2. A Talbot 'horseless carriage' (or car).
3. A man waving a red flag under the Red Flag Act (1865). This was to warn other road users of the possible dangers of the car.
4. False. 'Horseless carriages' did not supersede horses until the early 20th. century.
5. They were noisy, smelly, open to the weather and dangerous to the drivers and pedestrians. Only the upper classes, the very wealthy, could afford them.
6. Carl Benz and Gottlieb Daimler. No British inventors were involved.
7. In the countryside. No other traffic, country cottages, rural scene - trees, hedges.
8. See Teachers' Notes.
9. Catalogue - a complete, alphabetical list of items for sale; specifications - detailed description of the parts of the car; 4 lines - the company has 4 separate telephone numbers.

Page 73

1. Metal rod or crank turned to start the engine of a motor car. A battery operates a starting motor in modern cars.
2. Lamps with wax candles in them to provide light for driving. They would not have made driving easy because they would have given out very little light.
3. Ash wood. Tyres at the back were solid and pneumatic at the front. Pneumatic - refers to tyres with air in them. (Consider the tyres on modern cars today.)
4. Two. One.
5. The handbrake and a disk bolted to the back wheel. Drum brakes or disk brakes are used in modern cars. The brake drum or brake shoes or disk is forced against the rotating wheel. Pressure or force is applied to a hydraulic system (usually oil filled) and hence equally to all the brakes. (cf air brakes in lorries and brake pads on bicycles.)
6. In the middle of the vehicle. In front of the engine.
7. That the vehicle used a great deal of oil.
8. Yes. See Teachers' Notes.
9. True. It was one of the first motor cars with many new gadjets including a water cooled engine. Making the parts and getting all the various moving parts to work together was very difficult. Pneumatic tyres were an innovation. The construction of the car brought new technology together.
10. See Teachers' Notes.

Page 74

1. See Teachers' Notes. 2. See teachers' Notes.
3. (a) working class, (b) middle class, (c) middle class, (d) upper class, (e) working class, (f) working class, (g) working class, (h) middle class, (i) working class, (j) middle class.
4. See Teachers' Notes. 5. See Teachers' Notes.
6. See Teachers' Notes.

Page 75

1. It opened in Hyde Park in May, 1851 and stayed open for 26 weeks.
2. The Queen's Consort, Prince Albert.
3. Joseph Paxton. 4. The Crystal Palace.
5. See Teachers' Notes.
6. To exhibit the developments and technical progress made in industry and commerce.
7. 13,000 (a) 7,000 (b) 6,000. 8. 6 million people.
9. True. See Teachers' Notes.
10. Removed in 1851, rebuilt in Sydenham, South London. It was destroyed by fire in November, 1936.

Page 76

1. Victorian shop - A 2. B is easier.
3. For customers to sit on if they were tired: shopping was more leisurely than it is today. The chairs were obstructions, customers could fall over them and they took up space. Modern shops have restaurants/cafés where people can rest as well as changing rooms for babies.
4. Unhealthy, unhygienic. Customers may breathe over the food or handle it. The food may become contaminated.
5. Personal - A, impersonal - B.
6. Today shop owners do not want to remind customers of the time. They want the customers to stay and spend money.
7. To make customers feel relaxed and happy. It is believed to encourage customers to buy goods. There was no taped music available in Victorian times. Radio and the gramophone were in their infancy.
8. Shopping trolleys.
9. Victorian times - slow, salesman orientated, personal service, slow turnover, goods above eye-level and difficult to examine, unhygienic, cash taken slowly, fewer customers dealt with, goods not always priced, no bar codes, few shopping aids, small shops and little room, more limited choice, more local goods, little competition , no refrigeration ...

Today - fast, customer orientated, impersonal, fast turnover, goods placed so that they can be examined by customers, hygienic, cash taken quickly, large numbers of customers dealt with quickly, goods priced, bar codes, shopping aids (trolleys, packaging, carriers), supermarkets, plenty of room, wide choice, not only local goods, competition keeps prices down and maintains quality, refrigeration

Prefer today - faster, more choice, more hygienic, more room - see above.

Page 77

William Booth - Salvation Army.
Charles Darwin - wrote 'The Origin of Species'.
William IV - Victoria's uncle who reigned from 1830 - 1837.
Disraeli - Tory politician.
Lewis Carroll - wrote 'Alice In Wonderland'.
Gladstone - Liberal politician.
Dr. W. G. Grace - famous cricketer.

Page 77 cont.

Lord Shaftesbury - prison reformer.
Charles Dickens - wrote 'Oliver Twist'.
David Livingstone - famous African explorer.

Page 78

1. Anaesthetic, 2. back-to-back, 3. British Empire,
4. census, 5. cholera, 6. coronation, 7. governess,
8. home rule, 9. missionary, 10. monitor,
11. nanny, 12. penny farthing, 13. protectionism,
14. Rebecca riots, 15. slums, 16. suffragettes,
17. textiles, 18. tram, 19. transportation, 20. vaccination.

Page 79

1. Victoria's governess when she was a young child.
2. Benjamin Disraeli, Tory politician.
3. Florence Nightingale. 4. Turkey.
5. A piece of material or covering placed over the backs of chairs and settees to protect them from maccassar oil used by Victorian gentleman on their hair.
6. To care for orphans abandoned on London's streets.
7. William Booth.
8. (i) 24th. May 1819, (ii) 20th. June, 1837, (ii) 22nd. January, 1901.
9. Nearly 2.5 million people. 10. 31,000.
11. The death of the Prince Consort, Albert, from typhoid.
12. 1st. May 1851. 13. The Crimean War.
14. Southern Russian. 15. Charles Darwin.
16. Less than half the population of 18 million went to church.
17. Earl of Shaftesbury.
18. 1847 - limited the working hours of women and children to 10 hours a day.
19. True.
20. Schools first set up in 1844 for orphans and very poor children.
21. 1871.
22. Because of poor conditions in Ireland including the potato famines of 1845 and 1846.
23. Charles Stuart Parnell.

Page 80

DATE EVENT

1837 Victoria became Queen.
1840 Queen Victoria and Prince Albert married.
1842 Mines Act (children under 10 not allowed to work in mines).
1847 The Ten Hours Act (women and children 13 - 18 years old not allowed to work more than 10 hours a day).
1851 Great Exhibition held in Crystal Palace, London.
1861 Prince Albert died.
1863 First underground train in London.
1866 Nearly 6,000 people died in London from cholera.
1867 Dr. Thomas Barnardo founded the East End Juvenile Mission.
1870 Elizabeth Garrett Anderson became first woman doctor.
1872 First FA Cup Final.
1878 Salvation Army founded.
1891 First electric trains in London.
1897 Suffragette Movement started.
1899 Children had to attend school until they were 12.
1901 Queen Victoria died.

Page 81

1. Upper class - no occupation shown, a gentleman landowner.
2. Middle class - working solicitor, his wife stays at home, and he employs several servants.
3. Working class - worked for their living, not regarded as professional men (chemist/druggist was' in trade' and did not have the standing of law/solicitor). Employed one or two 'lower' servants.
4. They had large families and employed servants.
5. The wife did not work because - educated to run the home, numerous pregnancies and children, no labour saving devices, not educated or trained for business, commerce or teaching, the only employment would have been as a servant in another household, woman took the status of her husband, not socially acceptable for the wife to work outside the home, families had to live within the husbands' incomes.

Today - women educated, smaller families, modern homes do not take up so much time, fashionable, additional income, cost of housing high - double salary means a high mortgage available, higher expectations.

6. 1. Children would not work and daughters would be expected to make good marriages.
2. Son - trainee solicitor. Daughters would be expected to marry well.
3. Son - follow father into business - trainee druggist. Daughter - marry well or become a governess/nanny.
4. Sons - become manual workers. Daughters - marry/ may go into domestic service.

Page 82

1. Working class families.
2. Back-to-back. See Teachers' Notes.
3. Wealthy factory or mine owners/industrialists built the houses for their workers.
4. The location of industries and factories. Workers had to live within walking distance of their place of employment.
5. To carry water. There was no tapped water to these dwellings and water was carried from wells, streams and rivers.
6. Because of the work available in the new industries.
7. Unhealthy, unhygienic conditions in which disease thrived and spread leading to early death - see Teachers' Notes.
8. In the countryside away from the slums of the towns. See Teachers' Notes.

Page 83

1. No privacy, little room, danger of catching disease from other people.
2. True. Problems of carrying water, water contaminated transmitting disease.
3. Gas then electricity.
4. Slow, cumbersome, very few people could be carried in a carriage, horses had to be fed and watered, horses had to be stabled, people had to be trained to handle them ...
5. Gruel (thin porridge). Bread, cheese and gruel.
6. 19th Century - no schools provided. 20th. century - all children must attend achool.
7. Games at home, cards, dice, hoops, marbles, cock fighting, music hall ...
8. See Teachers' Notes.
9. Yes. See Teachers' Notes.

Page 84

A. Working in a textile factory.
B. Carrying clay to make bricks.
C. Sweeping roads.
D. Sweeping chimneys.
E. Opening a trap door and hauling coal in a mine.
F. Hauling coal.

Page 85

1. The child in passage A is employed in opening a trap door in a mine. Catherine Thompson in passage B hauls coal in carts for her father. David Gay is also employed to open and shut a trap door.
2. Cheap to employ (very low wages), small (they could where taller people could not), easily controlled and punished.
3. See passage.
4. Be attentive - listen carefully;
pull his string promptly - opens the door immediately someone come;
suffer for the same - be punished if he did not do his task correctly;
draw his coal - pull his father's cart full of coal.
5. A coal cart. 8 cwt of coal.
6. Her knee had been injured by a coal cart.
7. 12 hours.
8. He found it dificult to climb the stairs from the pit when he had finished.
9. A lift.
10. It is against the law. Children have to attend school.

Page 86

1. Patient A - smallpox, patient B - typhus, patient C - cholera, patient D consumption or tuberculosis.
2. See Teachers' Notes.
3. Smallpox. 4. Water.
5. They lived together in cramped and unhealthy conditions, used contaminated water and there was no regular removal of refuse.
6. Poor medical care including poor pre-natal care, poor food, poor living conditions, inexperienced and unhygienic doctors and nurses.
7. See Teachers' Notes. 8. See Teachers' Notes.
9. Factors include clean water supply, good food and balanced diet, sufficient sleep, regular exercise, trained medical care, warmth, education, good housing.
10. Own research.

Page 87

1. Votes for women.
2. The chains were a symbol of the status of women in society - they had few rights and no vote. They chains made it difficult for the police to remove the protestor.
3. The Suffragettes.
4. End of the 19th. century. Christabel Pankhurst, Eva Gore-Booth, Dorothea Beale.
5. To get the right to vote for all women over 21. See Teachers' Notes.
6. She was not in favour of it.
7.True.
8. See Teachers' Notes.
9. No. See Teachers' Notes.
10. See Teachers' Notes.

Page 88

A. Slate and slate pencils. B. Pen, ink and inkwell.
C. Abacus. D. Blackboard and easel.
E. School signal - a device used by teachers to get the attention of the pupils. F. Cane.
G. Dunces cap. H. School desk (and seat).
I. Globe. J. School bell.
K. School rules. L. Holy bible.

1. True. 2. False. 3. False. 4. True.
5. True. 6. True. 7. True. 8. False.
9. True. 10. False.

Page 89

1. A is the Victorian classroom. 2. B has most equipment.
3. **A, Victorian classroom:**
Older children, formal, children sitting in an orderly manner at their desks, whole class being taught the same thing, no equipment, children not experimenting, desks, children all doing the same things, children working in one group, silent.
B, classroom today:
Younger children, informal, children working on their own, indiviuals being taught, open plan, plenty of equipment, tables, children experimenting, children doing different things, children working in groups and individually, talking.
4. Both have teachers, both being taught.
5. The emphasis has changed to the individual needs of the child, less formal environment in the classroom today. [More understanding about how children learn. Also See Teachers' Notes.]
6. B. Many reasons - more interesting, more friendly, more informal, equipment, fun, easier to learn in this classroom ...

Page 90

A. 1. Punishment was harsh, indiscriminate and unfair - aimed to maintain discipline through fear.
2. The cane. They were afraid of being beaten.
3. No. Their main concern was to avoid punishment. They watched the cane and could not concentrate.
4. He had done all that he had to do.
He considered his job to be mainly punishing his pupils and keeping discipline rather than teaching.

B. 1. 'Evil' - non-attendance at school.
2. Masters, monitors, methods and systems are usually blamed.
3. 'Tap-root'- the main cause of the problem.
4. Mothers.
5. Mothers are not concerned about whether their children attend school or not. Any problem, however small, is a good enough excuse to keep their children away from school.
6. Yes, but parents today usually want their children to go to school.

Page 91

Reading, writing and arithmetic. They are very important today but children learn a wide range of subjects - the 3 Rs form the basic skills.
2. Dictation - writing out words or a passage as it is read out loud by the teacher as a spelling exercise. Drill - marching and other exercises usually carried out in the school yard. Sometimes there was desk drill. Dictation is used today, drill has been replaced by physical education.

Page 91 cont.

3. By using monitors. Fairly satisfactory for rote learning but not for 'real' teaching.
4. Subjects which are the same include writing, arithmetic, reading, dictation and singing.
5. See Teachers Notes.
6. Yes. (But plenty of room here for discussion about local variations.)
7. By governesses, private tutors at the homes of their pupils.
8. Early educationalists - to teach children just as much as they needed to know according to their 'station' in life, i.e. their class. To inculcate religious ideas of piety and obedience. To maintain the status quo.
Today - to teach children the basic skills, a wide range of subjects, to stimulate thought, to help children to develop and grow intellectually.
9. They feared the working classes would become dissatisfied with their lot and revolt agains the government. Educated, the workers would demand rights, in particular, the vote and the right to elect their own leaders to parliament ... Advantages/disadvantages - basis of a long discussion involving such concepts as dissemination of information, political control, rights of individuals, role of politicians and parliaments, kind of society ...
10. Again basis for a long discussion. Both involve the teaching of basic skills and the meticulous recording of the progress of pupils. Today the range of subjects is wide and the aims are different. See answer 8 ...

Page 92

1. Reading, writing and arithmetic. Writing.
2. Teaching Children to Write.
Learning to Write.
3. (a) Taught to form letters in sand trays.
(b) Taught to form letters on a slate with a slate pencil.
(c) Taught to write with pen and ink in a copybook.
4. Slate pencils.
5. With water, a sponge and a small mop.
6. It was easy to clean and use again - it was cheap.
7. Ink powder was mixed with water. It was stored in large white enamel jugs and poured into inkwells by ink monitors.
8. It was watery and dripped off the pen making blots. It also took a long time to dry and was easily smudged.
9. It resembled the writing used by engravers on copper-plated goods.
10. Simple sentences - facts. See Teachers' Notes.
11. He shouted at them and punished them for their mistakes.
12. They made ink blotches on their work.
13. This was the time of 'payment by results'. School inspectors might have looked at the children's books and a teacher might have lost some of his salary if the work was unsatisfactory.
14. To make a serious mistake (of any kind - to spoil your record).
15. More important in Victorian times. Today there are numerous ways of communicating - pc, laser writer, E-mail, telephone, television ... [Even doctors' prescriptions are now produced in flawless script by computer!] Nevertheless the importance of good cursive writing should not be under estimated - personal, pleasure to receive handwritten letters. Self expression, not merely presentation, is important today ...

Page 93

1. Passage A - labourers; passage B - gentry.
2. Meal in A - meagre; meal in B - grand, excessive.
3. Neither but A is more balanced than B.
4. The group in A was very poor and lived in working class conditions. The group in B was wealthy and lived in grand style.
5. 'Knock off' - finish; 'unyoked' - untied;
'nosebags' - bags containing feed for the horses;
'munched' - chewed; 'morsel' - very small piece;
'bidden' - told; 'dessert' - sweet;
'up to the brim' - filled to the top; 'immense' - huge;
'ready to march on the disappearance of the fish of soup' - to be served immediately the fish and soup courses were finished.

Page 94

2. By wearing a whalebone corset which was laced tightly.
3. Bustles. 4. Crinolines.
5. Top hats, gloves, topcoats, cravats, walking sticks/canes.
6. A monocle. 7. Cravats.
8. They were dressed like adults. (Today, children have their own style of clothes.]
9. Middle or upper class. See Teachers' Notes.

Page 95

1. Sir Rowland Hill (1795 - 1879). It suggested that letters should bear an adhesive stamp and be delivered anywhere in Great Britain for one penny.
2. The penny black - because of its colour and price.
3. True - now collectors' items worth thousands of pounds.
4. Because they were the first stamps in the world.
5. Letters were important for business and commerce, especially for importers and exporters. They encouraged the spread of literacy as people wrote to friends and relatives. They enabled people to communicate quickly and cheaply.
6. The penny post introduced in 1840 was too cheap. People sent many letters but the price did not cover the post office's costs.
7. 1855.
8. In 1897 to mark the Diamond Jubilee of Queen Victoria's reign.
9. Victoria Regina - Queen Victoria.
10. (a) As much as one shilling (5p) which was very expensive. (b) one penny (1d - less than 0.5p).

Page 96

1A. This is the drawing of a prison ship designed to take convicted prisoners to Australia. One of the main forms of punishment was to send 'criminals' this distance so separating them permanently from their families, e.g. the Tolpuddle Martyrs. Many of these ships were moored for weeks or months in isolated places waiting to sail. Prisoners were put in chains and manacled together inside them. They lived in overcrowded and filthy conditions and were badly fed.

1B. This is a picture of a treadmill, a type of moving staircase designed to provide exercise for prisoners. The treadmill was operated by levers and inmates were forced to walk up and down this moving staircase. Prisoners were not allowed to speak to one another during this exercise.

2. In Victorian times, there was a great deal of poverty and much <u>crime</u> as a result. In the big cities like London, there were a great many <u>pickpockets</u> who made their living from

Page 96 cont.
mingling with and stealing from crowds in the streets. Some men organised bands of young children to pick the pockets of the wealthy. Criminals were not often caught because there was no organised police force until Sir Robert Peel founded his peelers. By 1839, there were police forces all over the country. Criminals were dealt with harshly. Many men and women were flogged or sent to prison. Some were sent abroad to Botany Bay in Australia. Many died in convict ships on the way. The ships were moored on isolated river banks or near unhealthy swamps and marshes. Prisoners were ill-treated: they were seldom fed and lived in overcrowded conditions in silence because they were not allowed to talk to each other.

Page 97
A 1. See Teachers' Notes.
2. See Teachers' Notes.
3. See Teachers' Notes.

B1. In the workhouse. 2. More food.
3. Surprise and horror.
4. He was very poor - patched clothes, no shoes.
5. Teacher.
6. Teacher.

Page 98
A
1. A convict.
2. In grey prison clothes, broken shoes, an old piece of cloth around his head and iron shackles on one leg.
3. Because the man looked so fierce and Pip thought he might kill him.
4. 'Give it mouth' - speak.
5. He was a man who was very poorly dressed, who had been battered and bruised, obviously ill-treated and probably hunted by prison warders.
B
1. Young and small.
He is described as a boy and was able to climb up the narrow flues of chimneys.
2. He had not attended school. Compulsory education did not come in until later.
3. There was no water laid on to houses; it had to be carried from wells or streams.
4. ' Dark flues' - blackened chimneys; 'elbows raw' - sore arms from rubbing against the walls of the chimneys.
5. He cried when he had to climb the chimneys because the hard walls hurt his knees and elbows and soot got into his eyes. He was nearly always hungry and beaten.
6. Played games with the other boys,
7. He took the beatings bravely without flinching. His master thought little of him and ill treated him.
8. Young children were forced to work in dangerous conditions. Their employers were harsh and cruel, paid them little and beat them regularly.
9. Young children had to go to school and were prohibited by law from being employed.

Page 99
1. Own research.
2. Tea. 3. Own research.
4. £2 in Victorian times would be worth about £90 today. This is slightly less than most manual workers earn today.
5. Victorian times (i) £3.13.6d (ii) £1.5s
Today (i) £3.13.6 = £3.675
Today this would be worth £3.675 x 45 = £165.38 (approx)
(ii) £1.5s = £1.25
Today this would be worth £1.25 x 45 = £56.25
6. Consultation would cost £1.125 x 45 = £50.63 (approx)
[The description of the treatment (or what is not offered) gives an interesting insight into dentistry at this time.]

Page 100
1. Lowest in 1851; highest in 1891.
2. See Teachers' Notes.
3. Earning for a year of 52 weeks = £7.2s.
Earnings for one week = £7.2s. ÷ 52 = 142s ÷ 52 = 2.7s (13p worth about £5.85 today.)
4. Earnings for a year of 52 weeks = £6.16s.
Earnings for one week = £6.16s ÷ 52 = 136 ÷ 52 = 2.6s (12.5 p worth about £5.63 today .)
5. Servants became more experienced and reliable.
6. Even allowing that food and board was provided, wages were very low in Victorian times, much lower than today. Servants also had very little time off, perhaps an afternoon a week or a day a month.
7. £24.12s (now worth about £1,107 a year - very low).
8. Servants from workhouses were expected to be 'rougher' and need more training.
They were so anxious to leave the workhouses that they were willing to accept lower wages.
The workhouse masters were keen to be rid of their charges and would agreet lower wages for them.

2.
1.No. The law does not allow young people to undertake such full time employment.
2. Cleaning the grate with a polish called 'blacking'. This contained lampblack, a fine form of carbon which is greasy and gives a shine to metal.
3. The punishment seems harsh. She should not have been slapped and the fine of one shilling was very high, about half a week's wage. A good scrubbing in probably a zinc bath does not sound much fun either. Still, she might have been given an afternoon off and she had been given a prayer book.
4. There were no formal obligations to give holidays to servants although these were sometimes negotiated at the start of employment. Holidays were mostly at the whim of the employer and were infrequent.

RECORD SHEET
VICTORIAN BRITAIN

Name ______________________________ **Age** ______________

Page	Master Copy		Page	Master Copy	
63	The Young Queen/Accession		81	Class and Family Life	
64	Queen Victoria		82	Housing Conditions	
65	*The Times Newspaper, 1837*		83	Housing	
66	Victorian Times		84	The Employment of Children	
67	Florence Nightingale		85	Children down the Mines	
68	Disraeli and India		86	Victorian Illnesses	
68	The Crimean War		87	Women's Rights	
69	A Victorian Magazine		88	Education	
70	The Rainhill Trials		89	Classrooms	
70	Queen Victoria's Train		90	Educational Sources	
71	The Rebecca Riots		91	Timetables and Curriculum	
72	The 'Horseless Carriage'		92	Writing	
73	Daimler 1899		93	Victorian Eating Habits	
74	Class in Victorian Times		94	Victorian Clothes	
75	The Great Exhibition, 1851		95	Postal Reform	
76	Shopping		96	Crime and Punishment	
77	Famous Victorians		97	The Workhouse	
78	A Victorian Dictionary Quiz		98	Victorian Literature	
79	A Victorian Quiz		99	Victorian Arithmetic	
80	Victorian Time-Line		100	Wages and Employment	

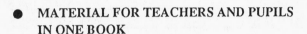

MASTER FILES ORDER FORM 1995

Quantity	Title	ISBN	Price	Cost
	MATHEMATICS (KS1)	1 85772 107 1	£20.00	£
	HISTORY (KS1)	1 85772 112 8	£20.00	£
	ENGLISH (KS1)	1 85772 111 X	£20.00	£
	SCIENCE (KS1)	1 85772 108 X	£20.00	£
	MATHEMATICS (KS2)	1 85772 086 5	£20.00	£
	ENGLISH (KS2)	1 85772 085 7	£20.00	£
	SCIENCE (KS2)	1 85772 087 3	£20.00	£
	HISTORY			
	Invaders and Settlers - The Celts (KS2)	1 85772 067 9	£15.95	£
	Invaders and Settlers - The Romans (KS2)	1 85772 070 9	£15.95	£
	Invaders and settlers - The Vikings (KS2)	1 85772 069 5	£15.95	£
	Victorian Britain (KS2/KS3)	1 85772 077 6	£15.95	£
	TOPICS			
	Castles (KS3)	1 85772 075 X	£15.95	£
	Christmas (Ages 5 - 12)	1 85772 065 2	£20.00	£
	New titles to be published monthly			
	Feb. 95 Life in Tudor Times (KS2)	1 85772 076 8	£15.95	£
	Feb. 95 Life in Stuart Times (KS2)	1 85772 081 4	£15.95	£
	Mar. 95 Invaders and Settlers - Anglo-Saxons (KS2)	1 85772 068 7	£15.95	£
	Mar.95 Britain since 1930 (KS2)	1 85772 078 4	£15.95	£
	April 95 The Roman Empire (KS2)	1 85772 083 0	£15.95	£
	May 95 Cathedrals (KS3)	1 85772 082 2	£15.95	£
	June 95 Prehistoric Britain (KS1)	1 85772 066 0	£15.95	£
	June 95 Life in Early Britain (KS2)	1 85772 120 9	£15.95	£
	July 95 The Second World War (KS2)	1 85772 121 7	£15.95	£
	July 95 The Present Day (KS2)	1 85772 122 5	£15.95	£
	July 95 Industrial Britain (KS3)	1 85772 123 3	£20.00	£
	July 95 The Twentieth Century World (KS3)	1 85772 124 1	£20.00	£

KS3 and KS4 Worksheets to be published monthly. Please send for details. **Total** £

School

Address

Tel.

Contact Signature

Order Number Date

Available from Foyles Bookshop, Foyles Educational, Welsh Books Council, Blackwells, Georges, Bookland, Dillons, Hammicks, Waterstones, WH Smith, Drake International Services and all good booksellers or direct from

DOMINO BOOKS (WALES) LTD, P O BOX 32, SWANSEA SA1 1FN

TEL. 01792 459378 FAX. 01792 466337

All official orders must have an official requisition form attached (schools, educational establishments, LEAs, bookshops, libraries). Cheques with private orders please.